# An Atlas of
# Polymer
# Damage

Surface examination by scanning electron microscope

Lothar Engel

Hermann Klingele

Gottfried W. Ehrenstein

Helmut Schaper

*Translated by* M. S. Welling

Wolfe Science Books
in association with
Carl Hanser Verlag, Munich, Vienna

Lothar Engel (Dipl.-Ing.)
Gerling Institute for Damage Research and Prevention, Cologne

Hermann Klingele (Dr.-Ing.)
Institute for Scanning Electron Microscopy, Munich

Gottfried W. Ehrenstein (Prof. Dr.-Ing.)
Kassel Highschool

Helmut Schaper (Dr.)
Head of Gerling Institute for Damage Research and Prevention,
Cologne

Title of the original German edition: 'Rasterelektronenmikroskopische
Untersuchungen von Kunststoffschaden'. 1978

English edition published by Wolfe Publishing Ltd,
3 Conway Street, London W1, in association with
Carl Hanser Verlag 1981
ISBN 0 7234 0751 7
Printed by Smeets-Weert, Holland

A companion volume to this book is An Atlas of Metal Damage,
also published by Wolfe Publishing Ltd in association with
Carl Hanser Verlag

# Contents

*continued*

# Preface

This Atlas shows the different kinds of damage shown by polymers, as seen under the scanning electron microscope. That damage can often be interpreted only by microscopic examination, for the success of which a familiarity with the appearance of such damaged surfaces at high magnification is needed. The Atlas is intended as a reference book which will enable those concerned with damaged polymer surfaces to identify the type of damage and to discover the underlying cause.

Detailed scientific discussions have been omitted since the book is aimed primarily at the practical engineer and only a brief summary of those polymer properties which are most important in assessing damaged surfaces is given.

The samples examined mainly originated from laboratory tests, and the SEM examinations were carried out by Lothar Engel and Hermann Klingele, whose comprehensive knowledge of, and experience in, the assessment of damaged metal surfaces proved to be an important asset. Their 'Atlas of Metal Damage' is a companion volume to this work.

The illustration of so many damaged polymer surfaces was possible only because many firms and their employees, especially those working in the laboratories of BASF Ludwigshafen, generously provided samples (for details see the Appendix). To all these we extend our sincere thanks.

Helmut Schaper, Cologne

# 1. Structure, properties and processing of polymeric materials

## Structure

The term 'plastics' which is commonly used throughout the English-speaking world, means 'polymeric materials' to the materials technologist and this is the term used in this book since it more clearly expresses the character of these substances.

Polymeric materials are generally understood to be materials which consist essentially of macromolecular organic compounds, so-called macromolecules, produced synthetically from simple, low molecular weight compounds such as ethylene, vinyl chloride etc, i.e. so-called monomers, or made by the conversion of high molecular weight organic natural products such as cellulose.

In their simplest form macromolecules are produced by the arrangement of monomer units in the form of threads or chains. The chain-type structure applies to macromolecules insofar as it characterises a structure consisting of separate elements with a certain degree of flexibility in relation to each other. The links of the chain are held together by chemical bonds. One can visualise the chain structure of a macromolecule by imagining it as a number of spheres which are joined and which represent the individual atoms, as shown in **1a**. Linear, thread-like macromolecules such as shown in **1b** tend towards an equilibrium state of a haphazard tangle (**1c**) if they are not subjected to external forces.

Since there are so many different ways in which monomers can react with one another, the production of a macromolecule – whether by polymerisation, poly-addition or polycondensation – can result not only in linear but also branched and cross-linked molecules, as shown in **2**. In the case of cross-linkage, the material is made up of one single macromolecule or molecular framework. The cross-links and branches are formed by chemical bonds (also referred to as primary bonds). The linkage energy varies between 200 and 600kJ/mol, depending on the type of monomer. The distance between the centres of bound atoms is between 0.075 and 0.3nm. Primary bonds can only be broken irreversibly.

Linear and branched macromolecules are physically held together by intermolecular forces, i.e. van der Waals' forces and hydrogen bonds, or secondary bonding. Their bond energy is between 2 and 20kJ/mol. The distance between the centre points of molecules or groups of atoms held together by such intermolecular forces is around 0.3–1nm.

Since the strength of secondary bonds is only about one-hundredth of that of the chemical bonds, they can be broken relatively easily by chemical or physical influences, e.g. solvents, water, heat. Thus, increasing temperature, for example, causes the thermal vibrations of the macromolecules to increase and thereby reduces the effect of the secondary bonds until these are weakened to such an extent that the cohesion of the macromolecules is broken down (softening, melting). At sufficiently high temperatures the individual chain molecules are mobile with respect to each other, the material can be plastically deformed and can be regarded as a highly viscous fluid. This process is reversible: as the material cools down, the effect of the secondary bonds increases once again (solidification, crystallisation). This type of behaviour is called thermoplasticity and polymeric materials consisting of linear or branched chain molecules are referred to as *thermoplastics*.

In three-dimensionally cross-linked macromolecules secondary bonding between adjacent chain sections is likewise present and this is affected by elevated temperatures. However, at high temperatures, i.e. above the softening point, the properties of these materials are largely governed by the chemical bond network which is fixed spatially as well as in respect to time, since the macromolecules cannot move freely with respect to each other and their flow is only limited. Here one speaks of *thermosets* or *elastomers*, depending on the density of the points of cross-linkage, i.e. the length of the chains between the cross-linkage points.

Thermoplastics are normally hard at room temperature, softening and becoming plastic when heated. This process is reversible, i.e. they become hard again on cooling. Typical thermoplastics include polyethylene (PE), polypropylene (PP), polyvinyl chloride (PVC), polystyrene (PS) and polyamide (PA).

**1**

(Diagram a is from Kunststoff-Werkstoffe im Gespräch, Aufbau und Eigenschaften, BASF, Ludwigshafen)

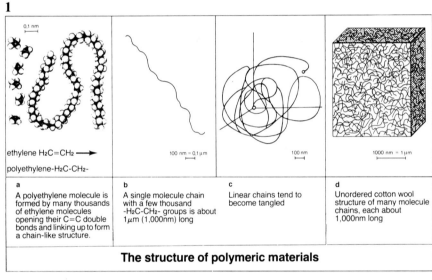

ethylene H₂C=CH₂ ⟶

polyethylene-H₂C-CH₂-

| a | b | c | d |
|---|---|---|---|
| A polyethylene molecule is formed by many thousands of ethylene molecules opening their C=C double bonds and linking up to form a chain-like structure. | A single molecule chain with a few thousand -H₂C-CH₂- groups is about 1μm (1,000nm) long | Linear chains tend to become tangled | Unordered cotton wool structure of many molecule chains, each about 1,000nm long |

**The structure of polymeric materials**

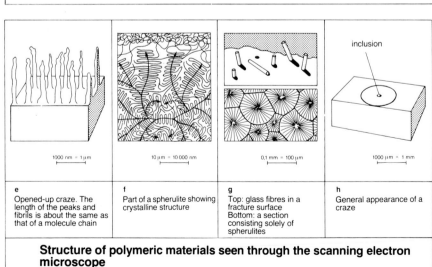

| e | f | g | h |
|---|---|---|---|
| Opened-up craze. The length of the peaks and fibrils is about the same as that of a molecule chain | Part of a spherulite showing crystalline structure | Top: glass fibres in a fracture surface. Bottom: a section consisting solely of spherulites | General appearance of a craze |

**Structure of polymeric materials seen through the scanning electron microscope**

*Thermosets* consist of macromolecules between which cross-linking is frequent. Secondary bonding is also present. Thermosets are hard at room temperature and they cannot be softened and made plastic by heating because the macromolecules are held together by chemical forces, even if the secondary bonds are weakened by the high temperature. Typical thermosets include cross-linked, i.e. cured phenolic resins (PF), aminoplastics (UF, MF), unsaturated polyesters (UP) and epoxy resins (EP).

*Elastomers* consist of macromolecules between which cross-linking is less frequent. As with thermosets, there are additional secondary bonds, whose effect is already non-existent at room temperature. Elastomers therefore exhibit rubber-like properties. They cannot be made plastic by heating. Typical elastomers include cross-linked polyisoprene as natural rubber (NR) or synthetic rubber (IR), polybutadiene (BR), styrenebutadiene copolymers (SBR) and polyurethane (PUR).

Macromolecules produced from only one basic unit (perhaps quite complex structurally) are called homopolymers; those produced from several different types of unit are referred to as copolymers. Linear or slightly branched (possibly also slightly cross-linked) macromolecules with a regular structure can develop lattice-type formations called crystallites. This occurs with certain thermoplastics such as polyethylene (PE), polypropylene (PP), polyamide (PA), polytetrafluoroethylene (PTFE) and others.

Industrially produced macromolecules always contain certain irregularities in their molecular structure (e.g. chain ends, double bonds, oxidised groups). Since a completely parallel arrangement is not possible, even for linear chain molecules, because of the tangled nature of the melt, even polymeric materials with a largely regular structure can only partially crystallise. The degree of crystallisation of the most important industrial polymeric materials is between 20% and 80%. When regularly constructed macromolecules crystallise, folding-up of the thread-like molecules is commonly encountered, presumably for energy reasons, so that blocks or lamellae are formed (**1f**). Their size is between 5 and 50nm in height (chain direction) and around 50nm wide and deep. Rapid cooling inhibits crystallites being formed. The non-crystalline chain segments of a macromolecule retain a more or less disordered structure and are referred to as being amorphous (**1d** and **3**).

In properly crystallised polymeric materials the greater part of the amorphous zones

**2**

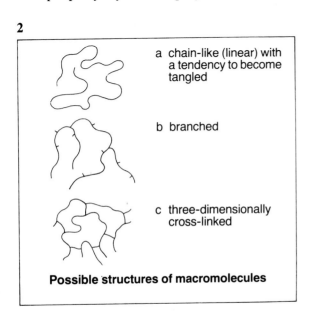

a chain-like (linear) with a tendency to become tangled

b branched

c three-dimensionally cross-linked

**Possible structures of macromolecules**

**3**

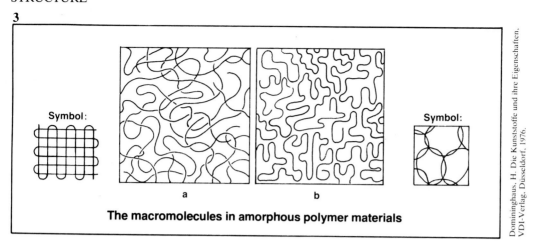

Domininghaus, H. Die Kunststoffe und ihre Eigenschaften, VDI-Verlag, Düsseldorf, 1976.

Symbol:

Symbol:

a

b

**The macromolecules in amorphous polymer materials**

is found at the surfaces of the crystallites (folds, chain ends, chain molecules passing from one crystallite to the next etc.), see **1f**. The edges of the crystallites (parallel to the chain direction), on the other hand, should be regarded as particle boundaries*. Partially crystalline polymeric materials are said to have a two-phase structure (crystalline-amorphous), a model which sufficiently explains many material properties.

The lateral boundary areas are centres of crystal growth and, after the formation of a stable crystallite, other crystallites grow to form sheaves **1f**. The simultaneous growth of many sheaves and their three-dimensional arrangement results in the often observed spherulitic structure shown in **1g**. The properties of partially crystalline polymeric materials depend more on the spherulites as an overall structure than on the individual crystallites of which they are composed.

Thermosets and (with a few exceptions) elastomers are always amorphous. Thermoplastics with a very irregular chain structure cannot crystallise either, as already mentioned. This type of amorphous thermoplastic includes materials such as polycarbonate (PC) and polystyrene (PS).

Non-crystalline polymeric materials solidify at low temperatures because secondary bonding becomes active, resulting in the irregular chain formation (tangled mass) being frozen. One here refers to a supercooled melt or – analogous to silicate terminology – the glassy state. In the temperature range in which solidification occurs lies the glass transition temperature $T_g$, which is defined by the main maximum of the mechanical loss factor d (**7**). The solidification process is reversible and the temperature at which the material softens is called the softening point.

# Homogeneous polymeric materials

Agreement as to when exactly a polymeric material may be regarded as homogeneous depends on the manner in which the material is assessed. The above remarks concerning the structure of partially crystalline thermoplastics have shown that structural inhomogeneities (crystallites, particle boundaries, amorphous regions, spherulite boundaries) occur in polymeric materials which are largely homogeneous from the chemical standpoint. The melt and amorphous glassy state, on the other hand, are structurally homogeneous. The same applies to copolymers made from different monomers and polymer blends with good compatibility.

We shall therefore regard as homogeneous all those polymeric materials which macro-

*Glenz, W. (Personal communication).

scopically have the same properties at all points. Differences in properties caused by different types of molecules cannot be ascertained macroscopically. Thus, according to this definition, most polymeric materials are homogeneous.

# Heterogeneous polymeric materials

Heterogeneous polymeric materials consist of at least two chemically different substances, one of which is a coherent polymeric material. The substances, combined in macroscopic units, can be bound to each other chemically or physically. The properties of heterogeneous polymeric materials are decisively determined by the separate components.

*Rubber modified polymers*
To increase impact strength, it is customary to incorporate rubber particles in the base material, the aim being to achieve uniform distribution of the rubber particles (e.g. butadiene (BR), acrylate rubber, EPDM etc.) in the polymer (e.g. polystyrene (PS), styrene-acrylonitrile copolymer (SAN) etc.). Since these two types of component are largely incompatible, separation occurs, during which uniformly dispersed rubber particles are formed in the coherent matrix, these rubber particles themselves often containing small amounts of the matrix substance. Figure 4 shows a section through a particle of a rubber modified, impact resistant polystyrene (SB).

**4**

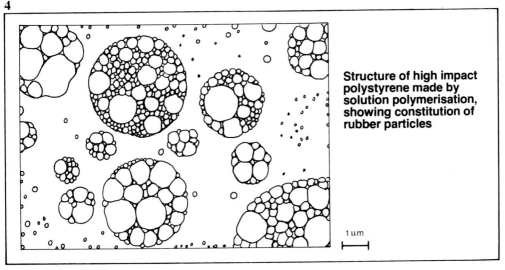

Structure of high impact polystyrene made by solution polymerisation, showing constitution of rubber particles

1 um

Stabenow, J. and Haaf, F Morphologie von ABS-Pfropf-Kautschuken. Angewandte Makrom. Chemie. Bd. 29/30 (1973) S. 1/23.

*Composite materials*
The most important heterogeneous composites are glass fibre reinforced polymeric materials (GRP). The rigidity and strength of polymeric materials are less than those of glass by a factor of about 25. On the other hand the thermal expansion of glass is about 25 times smaller than that of plastics. The values for elongation at break are of the same order. The diameter of the individual glass fibres is normally around $10\mu$m. They are used either in the form of chopped glass fibres, 0.1–0.5mm long, for reinforcing thermoplastics, or as filaments about 50mm long and consisting of several hundred such fibres collected together, or in the form of fibre mats, for the reinforcement of thermoset casting resins.

The starting product for the three most important kinds of glass fibre reinforcement for casting resins are strands consisting of at least 200 glass filaments bundled together which are then converted into woven glasscloth, woven rovings (30 or 60 strands) or mats, as shown in **5**. Mats consist of 50mm long, haphazardly arranged, chopped strands, or of strands arranged in loops. Glass fibres must be sized before they can be fabricated, i.e. treated with sizes which contain adhesion promoters, polymeric film formers and wetting agents. The function of the first component is to improve the adhesion between the organic resin matrix and the inorganic glass fibres.

**5**

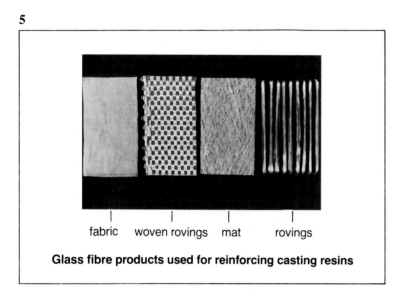

fabric    woven rovings    mat    rovings

**Glass fibre products used for reinforcing casting resins**

# Behaviour on deformation

If an external force is made to act upon polymeric material it first of all deforms elastically or visco-elastically. When the load is removed, the elastic deformation completely and spontaneously disappears. The visco-elastic deformation also disappears completely, but takes longer to do so. If the force exceeds a certain threshold, permanent, i.e. irreversible, deformation occurs.

A special feature of the deformation behaviour of polymeric materials is that the macromolecules not only react spontaneously to the applied load but that the individual molecule chains aim at degrading the stresses by some sort of rearrangement until an equilibrium value has been attained (relaxation)*. The loads of the individual chains when the stress is applied, and their molecular rearrangement possibilities, are different. The speed at which these rearrangement processes take place depends not only on the amount of stress and the rate at which it is applied, but also on the structure and temperature of the polymeric substance. Chain mobility is determined by physical and chemical bonds as well as by bulky side groups. If the material is heated, vibrations will increase as will the size of the empty spaces, facilitating the rearrangement processes of the molecules. If the loading period is short compared with the time taken for molecular rearrangement, the polymeric material will be brittle and rigid. If, on the other hand, the rearrangement mechanisms are able to degrade the applied loads within the period of loading until an equilibrium value is reached, the polymeric material will be tough and flexible.

One and the same polymeric material can therefore exhibit brittle or tough deformation behaviour at different temperatures or loading speeds (**6**).

*Retting, W. Viskoelastisches Verhalten bei zügig wachsender Spannung und Verformung, from Schreyer: Konstruieren mit Kunststoffen, Carl Hanser Verlag, Munich 1972.

**6**

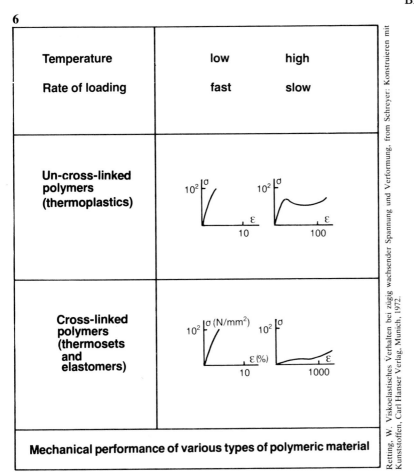

| Temperature | low | high |
|---|---|---|
| Rate of loading | fast | slow |
| **Un-cross-linked polymers (thermoplastics)** | $10^2$ $\sigma$ / $\varepsilon$ / 10 | $10^2$ $\sigma$ / $\varepsilon$ / 100 |
| **Cross-linked polymers (thermosets and elastomers)** | $10^2$ $\sigma$ (N/mm$^2$) / $\varepsilon$ (%) / 10 | $10^2$ $\sigma$ / $\varepsilon$ / 1000 |

**Mechanical performance of various types of polymeric material**

Retting, W. Viskoelastisches Verhalten bei zügig wachsender Spannung und Verformung, from Schreyer: Konstruieren mit Kunststoffen, Carl Hanser Verlag, Munich, 1972.

*Physical states of polymeric materials*

When thermoplastics are heated, the intermolecular secondary bonds are gradually overcome as the temperature increases, due to increased molecular movement, so that the material becomes like a more or less viscous fluid (plastic range). In the case of amorphous thermoplastics, the softening phase is followed by a relatively stable phase, i.e. one where material properties are not much affected by temperature. This rubber-like state is due to a phenomenon known as entropy-elasticity. Only far above the softening range (about 50–70°C) do amorphous thermoplastics begin to flow. Partially crystalline thermoplastics start to flow only above the melting point of the crystallites ($T_m$) and in this state thermoplastics are readily deformed. As the material cools, the secondary bonding again becomes effective. This reversible process can be repeated indefinitely, as long as there is no thermal degradation of the macromolecules, i.e. chain degradation, **7**.

The softening process can be clearly seen by the change in shear modulus. Here, amorphous thermoplastics (**7a**) behave differently to partially crystalline thermoplastics (**7b**). In the case of partially crystalline thermoplastics only the amorphous zones soften at the glass transition temperature $T_g$, whereas the crystalline zones are still hard. The higher the degree of crystallisation the less marked will be the drop in shear modulus in the softening range. As **7b** shows, these materials have a rigidity and dimensional stability that is often adequate for practical purposes above the softening point, until the crystallite melting point $T_m$ is reached.

The characteristic difference between thermosets and thermoplastics is that the shear modulus of thermosets hardly changes above the softening point until the decomposition temperature $T_d$ is reached. The same also applies to elastomers although in this case the proportion of chemical cross-linkage is less, so that the material is softer.

**7**

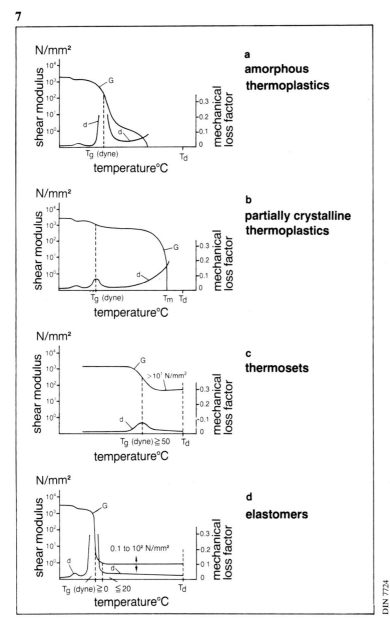

**7.** The variation of shear modulus G and the mechanical loss factor d with temperature for various polymeric materials.

$T_g$ = glass transition temperature of the amorphous regions.
$T_d$ = decomposition temperature.
$T_m$ = melting point of the partially crystalline regions.

# Processing

The important consideration as far as processing of polymeric materials is concerned is their chemical condition and physical state of aggregation. Manufacturers supply the raw materials either as polymers which are converted by moulding (especially thermoplastics, usually supplied in granule or powder form) or as monomers which have to be polymerised and possibly cross-linked during the moulding process.

The raw materials are often first prepared by special methods, encompassing an operation known as compounding which involves the incorporation of additives such as fillers, reinforcing materials, plasticisers, stabilisers, pigments, lubricants, catalysts, nucleants, blowing agents etc.

Thermoplastics and thermosets can be relatively easily machined in their normal, hard state. Thermoplastic semi-finished products can be warmed until they soften and become flexible, when they can be formed with little effort. The shape produced under these conditions is retained as the article cools and becomes hard again. The fluid/viscous state (melt) may be regarded as an intermediate stage when forming under pressure at high temperatures.

Casting resins and pourable monomers (for cast polyamide) are supplied for room temperature processing in the liquid state, to make large volume articles.

## HIGH PRESSURE FORMING AT HIGH TEMPERATURES

Here one distinguishes between intermittent (compression, transfer and injection moulding) and continuous (extrusion, film blowing and calendering) processes.

### Compression moulding of thermosets

The compression moulding of thermosets involves converting the powdered, granular or coarse particle moulding compound – cold or pre-heated – into preforms which are placed in the heated mould, softened under heat and pressure and moulded into shape (compression moulding). The moulding compound can also be moulded in loose powder form. Chemical cross-linking occurs during this moulding process. Because of the short flow paths, high molecule mobility and molecular re-arrangement during cross-linking, there is less molecular orientation in compression moulding than there is in transfer and injection moulding. Laminates are made by impregnating flat sheets which may be paper, veneer, fabric, film, etc. with resin, cutting them to size and press moulding them*.

To press mould glass fibre reinforced casting resins, the two components – glass fibre reinforcement and resin/catalyst mix – are introduced into the mould in the form of prepregs (i.e. pre-impregnated glass fibre) or separately.

Whereas compression moulding involves putting the moulding compound straight into the mould cavity, in transfer moulding the material is first heated in a transfer chamber to soften it, from where it is forced into the closed mould.

### Injection moulding

In injection moulding the granules are continuously melted in a heated cylinder and injected intermittently into a mould which is normally cooled but which may be heated if necessary for certain types of application. A heated mould, for example, induces higher crystallinity. The injection pressure is maintained until the material has set sufficiently so as not to flow out of the mould when the pressure is released. In this way voids and sink marks are prevented. Complex mould and feed systems cause materials containing fibrous and platelet-like fillers to show marked orientation. Injection mouldings have very good dimensional accuracy and can be made with smooth and glossy, textured or engraved surfaces, depending on the inside mould surface.

*Knappe, W. and Rainer, V. Kunststoff-Verarbeitung, from: Kunststoff-Handbuch Bd. 1 Grundlagen, Carl Hanser Verlag, Munich, 1975.

## Extrusion

Extrusion consists of forcing the plasticised, i.e. softened compound through a die continuously by means of a rotating screw. The die shapes the extrudate, which is calibrated before it sets solid. Calibration accurately fixes the extrudate dimensions – in the case of hollow shapes outside and/or inside, **8**. Extrusion is used to make solid and hollow shapes, flat sheets, longitudinally and transversely corrugated sheets, cable sheathing and wire coverings, and film. The extruder fulfils three essential tasks: drawing in the powdered or granular polymeric material, heating, melting and compacting it to form a homogeneous melt, and forcing the melt out through a suitable die. During extrusion, molecular orientation occurs in the extrusion direction. The lower the temperature and the higher the flow rate of the melt, the greater will be the orientation which takes place in the material.

**8**

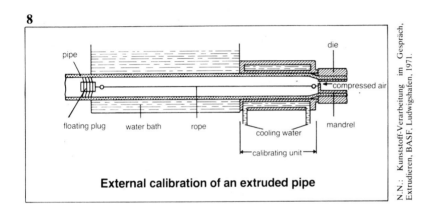

**External calibration of an extruded pipe**

N.N.: Kunststoff-Verarbeitung im Gespräch, Extrudieren, BASF, Ludwigshafen, 1971.

## Blow moulding, blown film extrusion, sheet polishing

Extrudates are often subjected to further fabricating and conversion processes in a second unit which is coupled to the extruder. The most important processes involved are blow moulding and blown film extrusion, as well as the production of polished extruded sheets.

In blow moulding a tube, called parison, is extruded continuously, or intermittently from an accumulator adjacent to the extruder, into a cooled mould where it is inflated as shown in **9**.

Blow mouldings have different inside and outside surfaces, the latter being determined by the inside surface of the mould. Streaks are often seen on both surfaces in the extrusion direction. The most widely used material for blow moulding is polyethylene (PE) but polypropylene (PP) and polyvinyl chloride (PVC) are also used and, more rarely, nylon 6 (PA 6 ).

A variant of blow moulding is the continuous process known as blown film extrusion, in which a thin-walled extruded tube is inflated to several times its original diameter by blowing in air. After cooling, the resultant film bubble is pressed flat by two pinch rolls and wound up. The most important film blowing materials are polyethylene (PE) and polypropylene (PP). Polyvinyl chloride (PVC) and polystyrene (PS) can also be used.

Thicker sheets are extruded through slit dies and then passed through polishing rolls to polish and roll them out to exactly the required thickness. The sheets are then cooled, internal stresses being relieved at the same time.

## Calendering

Another method used to make sheets is calendering. The thermoplastic material is first plasticised on rollers or mixers and fed to a calender, between whose rolls it is sheeted out to form film, or sheets with gauges from 0.05 to 2mm. An embossed surface can be produced by passing the material through a pair of special embossing rolls. The first of the calender rolls are normally heated. Downstream cooling rolls harden the sheets.

**9**

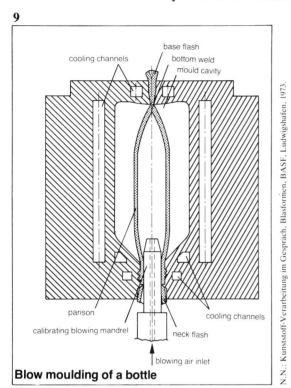

**Blow moulding of a bottle**

N.N.: Kunststoff-Verarbeitung im Gespräch, Blasformen, BASF, Ludwigshafen, 1973.

# LOW PRESSURE MOULDING

## Thermoforming

As **7** shows, the shear modulus of a material is greatly reduced above the softening point. In this region, the elongation at break shows a marked increase, which means that conditions for altering the shape of an article without applying much force are particularly favourable. In this process, called thermoforming, the heated sheet is stretched considerably and at those points which have been stretched most there will be a considerable reduction in wall thickness. To prevent this, the heated sheet material is often first stretched mechanically or pneumatically and thermoformed afterwards by vacuum or compressed air (**10**). As soon as the resultant moulded article has cooled down it sets hard. Generally speaking, the surface finish of thermoformed articles is not as good as that of injection mouldings.

## Casting

Liquid monomers can polymerise in moulds without pressure. Similarly, PVC pastes (plastisols) can be converted into solids by heating them, and causing fusion of the PVC particles and the plasticiser. In this way it is possible to produce thick-section articles using inexpensive moulds. Since, however, this technology is not without problems, only few polymeric materials are processed in this manner, notably epoxy

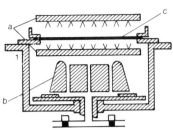

1 Heating-up the sheet to be thermoformed

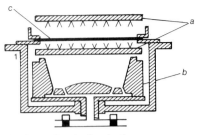

1 Heating-up the plastics sheet

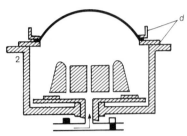

2 Pneumatic pre-stretching of sheet (optional)

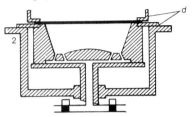

2 Applying the tool to the sheet

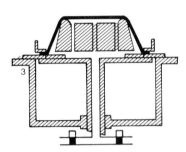

3 Mechanical pre-stretching of sheet (optional)

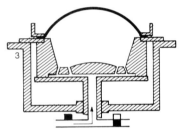

3 Pneumatic pre-stretching of sheet (optional)

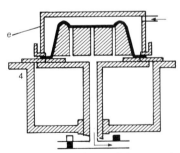

4 Thermoforming of the article by evacuating
the space between the sheet and the tool or
by compressed air in a pressure tank.
Cooling, followed by demoulding

*Positive forming (left)*
a heater; b positive tool; c plastics sheet;
d clamping frame; e pressure tank

*Negative forming (right)*
a heater; b negative tool; c plastics sheet;
d clamping frame; e pressure tank;
f pre-stretching tool

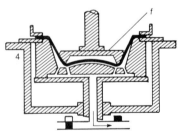

4 Mechanical pre-stretching of sheet (optional)

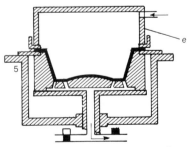

5 Thermoforming of the article by evacuating
the negative tool or by compressed air in a
pressure tank

## Thermoforming

**11**

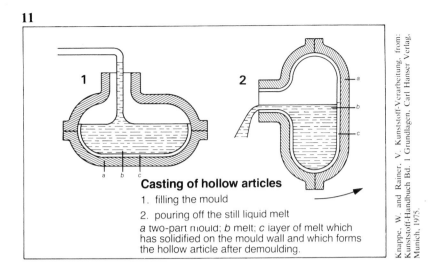

**Casting of hollow articles**
1. filling the mould
2. pouring off the still liquid melt
*a* two-part mould; *b* melt; *c* layer of melt which
has solidified on the mould wall and which forms
the hollow article after demoulding.

Knappe, W. and Rainer, V. Kunststoff-Verarbeitung, from: Kunststoff-Handbuch Bd. 1 Grundlagen, Carl Hanser Verlag, Munich, 1975.

resins, polyurethanes, cast polyamides and PVC pastes. A special technique is rotational moulding or centrifugal casting, used to make hollow articles, in heated, rotating moulds, as shown in **11**.

*Flame spraying and fluidised bed coating*
Protective coatings are often applied by flame spraying or electrostatic coating. A related technique is fluidised bed coating, in which powder particles are blown on to the heated article by a current of air. The particles fuse, flow and thus form a homogeneous coating.

*Dipping*
Articles can be coated by immersing them in polymer solutions or dispersions. The process is called dipping and is used either to permanently coat an article (dip coating) or to apply a coating which is then stripped off in the form of a finished article (dip moulding). The characteristic feature of the process is that the area to be treated is freely exposed.

*Processing of glass fibre reinforced casting resins*
The techniques used here may be classified into low and high pressure moulding, e.g. centrifugal casting, casting and continuous processes, and filament winding. Since the resins used are converted into solids only by adding suitable catalysts and, possibly, accelerators, at room or elevated temperatures, considerable influence is exerted by variables. During the moulding process uneven surfaces are possible, even if partly covered with film (hand lay-up, spray-up, vacuum moulding, filament winding, centrifugal casting). Smooth surfaces on both sides are likewise possible (some types of low and high pressure moulding, continuous methods of making sheets, pultrusion). The properties of the finished moulding are determined not only by curing conditions and formulation or mixing ratio, but also by the type of glass fibre reinforcement used (see also **5**) and the finish used to size the glass fibre material. Often well-dispersed small bubbles in the laminate cannot be avoided, especially in the hand lay-up, spray-up moulding and filament winding processes. A typical feature of many of the techniques used is the building-up of layer upon layer of pure resin and glass fibre reinforcing material.

## Foaming

Nearly all polymeric materials can be foamed or expanded when they are soft and plastic. Foaming is caused by gas produced during cross-linking, evaporating liquids, the incorporation of gases under pressure, or the addition of chemical blowing agents.

## Welding

Most thermoplastics can be welded. A number of methods can be used, details of which are outlined below.

Hot air welding: the surfaces to be joined, and the filler rod, are heated by air to melt them, and are then joined under pressure.

Heated tool welding: the material is partly melted with a heated metal tool which is often coated with a non-stick finish. The melted surfaces are then pressed together.

Heat sealing welding: used for welding most thin, flat materials by means of induction-heated welding bars which are applied to one or both sides of the material.

Friction welding: the pieces of material are made to rotate against each other. Heat is produced through friction, melting the material. The melted surfaces are then pressed together.

High frequency welding: the components to be welded, usually thin-section, are melted in an alternating electric field between two electrodes and joined under pressure.

Ultrasonic welding: in this method, which is related to friction welding and is used mainly for small parts, the energy is produced ultrasonically.

## Bonding

Certain thermoplastics (PS, SB, SAN, ABS, PVC, PA and PC) can only be bonded properly under certain conditions. There is often the risk of stress cracking. Thermosets on the other hand are generally easy to bond.

## Machining

Unfilled polymeric materials are easy to machine and polish. Because of their poor thermal conductivity, sharp tools should be used, the swarf should be thin and cutting speeds high. Coolants should be tested first in view of the possible danger of stress cracking. A special product made by machining solid, round shapes is gas permeable membranes.

## Post-moulding treatment

Surfaces of polymeric materials can be mechanically or chemically treated (flame treatment, electroplating, roughening, polishing, metallising) depending on the type of application for which they are intended.

# Orientation and internal stresses

Freely solidified polymer melts are largely homogeneous and isotropic. The moulding process however causes deformation of the macromolecules to occur, especially in the melted state and in the rubber-like state (above the softening point). This results in preferential orientation of molecule segments (see **240**). These orientations are of importance for thermoplastics but less so for thermosets where relatively little deformation is possible because of the chemical cross-linkage.

Molecular orientation is caused by external forces acting on the polymeric material, by deformation during cooling, polymerisation or the chemical cross-linking of the macromolecules. Orientation produced above the softening point is 'frozen-in' when the material cools down to below the softening point.

Orientation of molecule segments means a larger number of chains per cross-sectional area and therefore an increase in strength in the direction of deformation. At right-angles to the direction of deformation, on the other hand, the strength decreases (anisotropy of strength characteristics).

Orientation caused by processing, such as is produced, for example, during injection moulding, extrusion, blow moulding etc can never be completely prevented. In injection moulding, for example, one must always accept orientation in the direction of moulding, despite the very high moulding temperatures which go almost to the extreme limit. Pressed sheets, made from the same material, on the other hand are almost free from orientation. Such sheets are used to determine the standard for properties of the material.

Orientation occurs mainly at points where high shear stresses during processing cause molecule deformation which is then frozen-in through rapid cooling. Because of the poor thermal conductivity of polymeric materials, orientation due to processing is confined mainly to small areas, namely those close to the mould wall, which cool rapidly. A high degree of orientation at the surface of a polymeric material usually means increased susceptibility to stress cracking.

Internal stresses are stresses which are present in a component in the absence of external forces. They can be produced through cooling, holding pressure during injection moulding, the presence of foreign particles, crystallisation, swelling and hardening. Heating polymeric material where orientation is present can also result in the formation of internal stresses. When a polymeric material is heated above its softening point, deformed molecule parts tend to revert to their tangled form. If this tendency differs from point to point, internal stresses are produced.

Internal stresses are highest immediately after their formation and are then most dangerous for the component. They are degraded in time, through relaxation, a process that is accelerated by heating. Whether or not internal stresses cause fracture depends on whether, during the course of the envisaged life of an article, the sum total of external forces acting on the article and its internal stresses will at all times be less than its strength.

# Surface texture due to the manufacturing process

In order to be able to judge damage to polymeric material surfaces, it is necessary to be familiar with the surface textures that are caused by the manufacturing process. Here one must distinguish between primary textures due to the manufacturing process and those due to subsequent treatment of surfaces.

## PRIMARY TEXTURES OF POLYMER SURFACES DUE TO THE MANUFACTURING PROCESS

**Thermoplastic surfaces**

Thermoplastics are supplied to moulders in granular and powder form, **12–19**. The surface finish of articles made from these materials is governed by the moulding process.

*Injection moulding.* The surfaces carry the negative impression of the inside mould surface.

*Extrusion.* The surface finish is determined by the surface of the die, the reversion of oriented molecules to the tangled state and associated formation of small knots, and finally, the calibrating process.

*Calendering.* The surface finish is determined by the nip at the calender rolls and the surface of the polishing rolls.

*Blown film extrusion.* The surface texture of thin blown film is not caused by any mechanical contact.

*Blow moulding.* The outside wall is a replica of the inside of the blow mould, the inside wall represents a free, i.e. open surface. Since the contact pressure between the article and the mould wall is slight, the impression of the mould surface is only faint.

*Foaming.* The external surface finish is determined by the mould. If the foam is cut, the foam structure will be exposed and form the surface.

**12–14.** Powder particle of high molecular weight HDPE as supplied. The approximately $0.05\mu$m thick, thread-like and flat formations are presumably crystalline structures. (100:1; 5,000:1; 20,000:1)

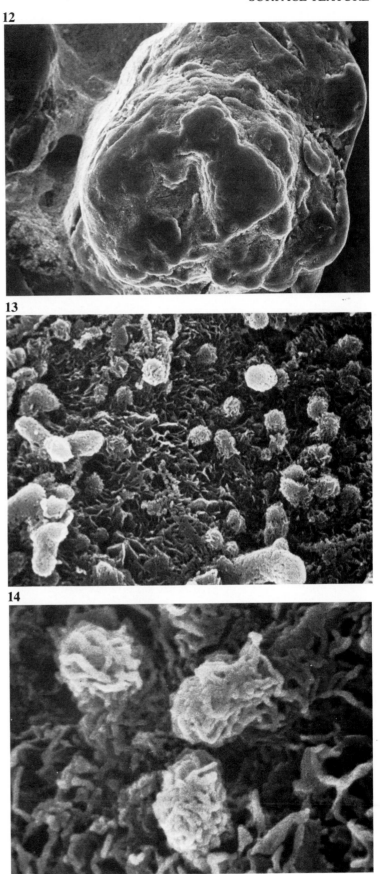

**15, 16.** Individual particles of suspension PVC powder in the primary polymerised state. (500:1; 5,000:1)

**15**

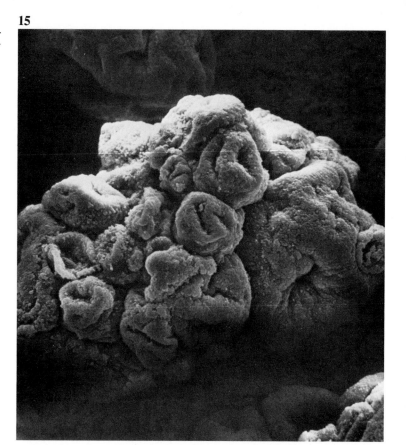

**16**

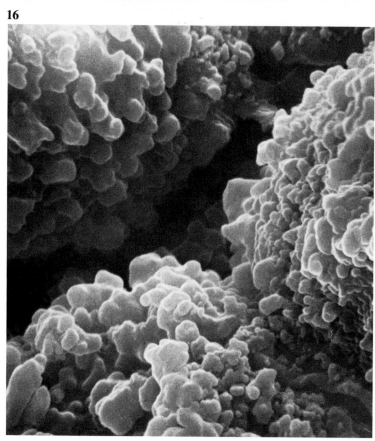

**17.** Emulsion PVC powder, surface of a spherical agglomerate with a diameter of 0.5mm. (20,000:1)

17
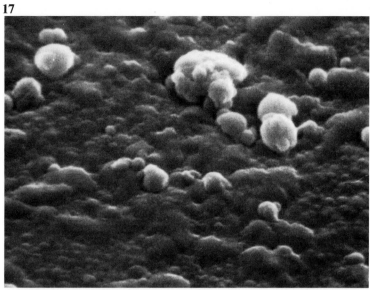

**18.** Emulsion PVC powder, fracture surface of a spherical agglomerate with a diameter of 0.5mm. (20,000:1)

18
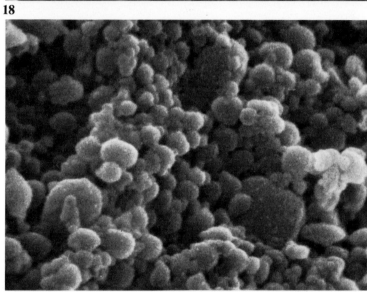

**19.** PVDF Primary particles. (21,000:1)

19
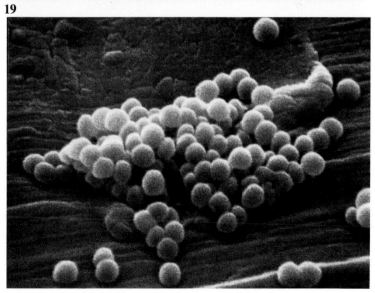

**20, 21.** A sealing ring made from injection moulded nylon 66 clearly reproduces the grooves made by machining the mould. (100:1; 500:1)

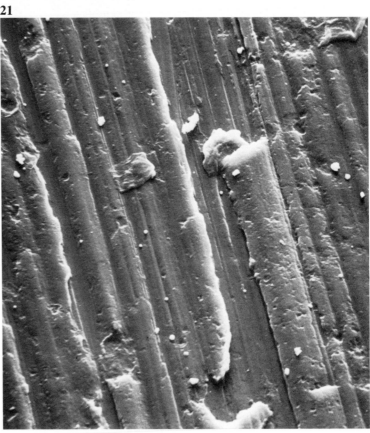

**22, 23.** Surface of a nylon container, the texture being due to the manufacturing process, and a negative impression of the injection mould. This is particularly apparent in the raised ridges. (540:1; 5,400:1)

22

23

**24, 25.** Surface of an extruded PVC sheet. The texture consists of small knobs and knots which are due to the basic structure of the polymer (cf. **16**). (1,000:1; 10,000:1)

**24**

**25**

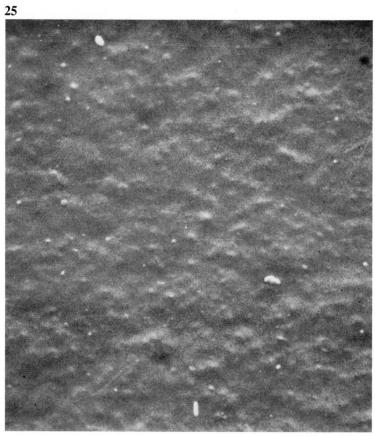

**26, 27.** Surface texture of extruded and compression moulded PP sheets with wood flour. The roughness of the material itself has had superimposed on it the negative impression of the mould surface. The texture of the wood flour cannot be seen on the closed surface. (2,200:1; 2,200:1)

**26**

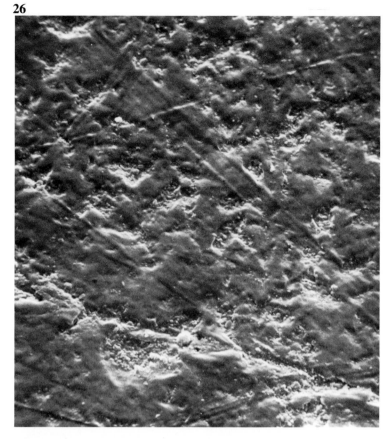

**27**

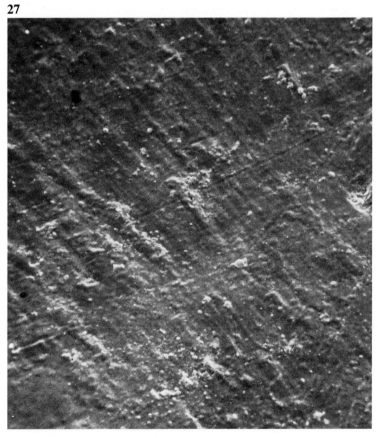

**28, 29.** Surface texture of compression moulded HDPE sheet, produced by the negative impression of the mould surface as well as by the movement of the moulding compound relative to the mould walls. This can be seen by the overlapping parts. (2,200:1; 5,400:1)

**28**

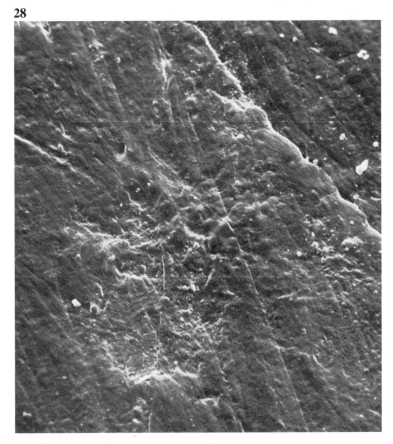

**29**

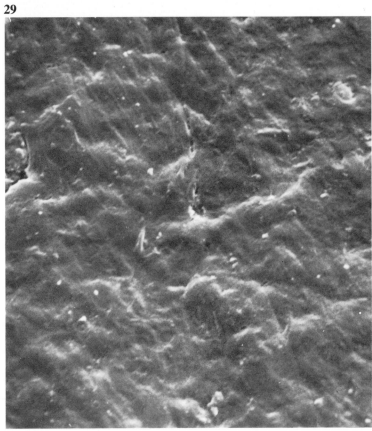

**30, 31.** Internal (**30**) and external (**31**) surface of a thermo-formed ABS specimen. The surface is determined by primary structures (rubber particles). (10,000:1; 10,000:1)

**30**

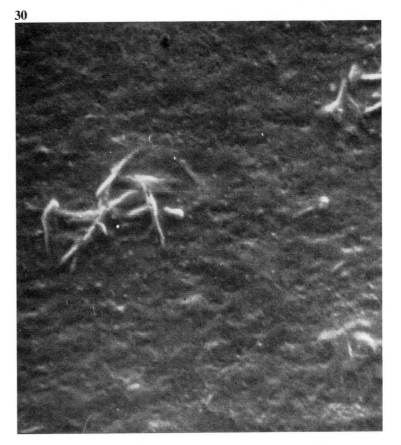

**31**

**32, 33.** Internal surface of a blown PS bottle, showing a knot-like texture. (200:1; 12,000:1)

**32**

**33**

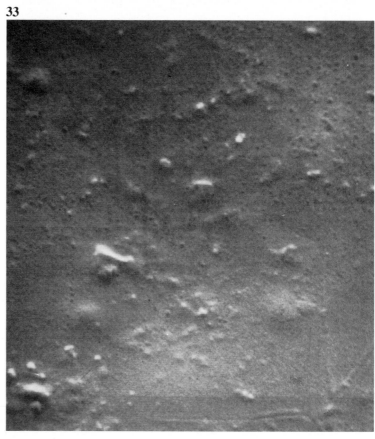

**34, 35.** External surface of a blown PS bottle, showing a knot-like texture overlaid by a fine mineral dust (particle size 1μm) probably deposited during extrusion of the parison. (200:1; 12,000:1)

**34**

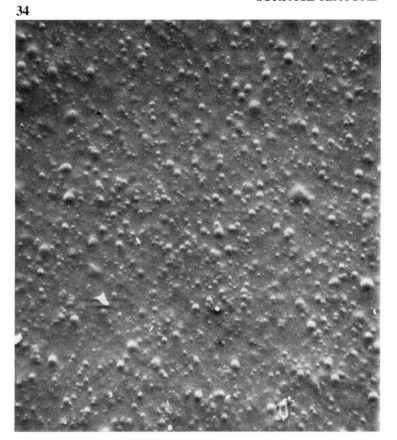

**35**

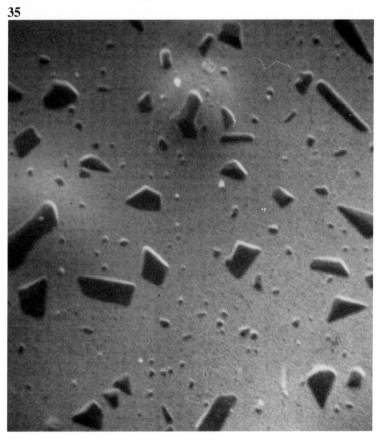

**36, 37.** Internal surface of a blown HDPE container, showing texture due to the manufacturing process. Partially crystalline structure with spherulite formation. (2,200:1; 5,200:1)

**36**

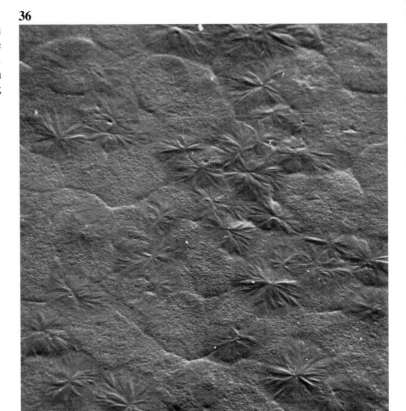

**37**

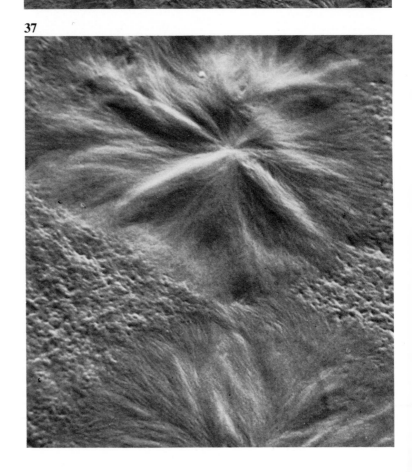

**38, 39.** Internal surface of a blown HDPE bottle, fresh from the factory, used to store washing water for a car. This shows a gently undulating surface and lamellar pattern, probably of crystalline structure. (220:1; 2,200:1)

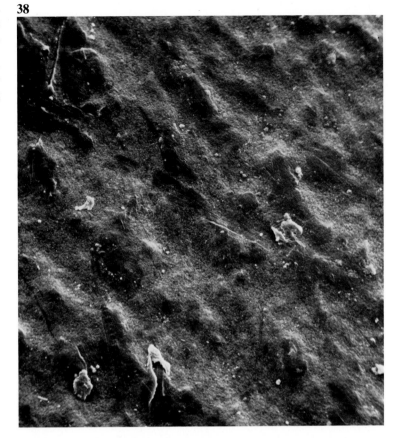

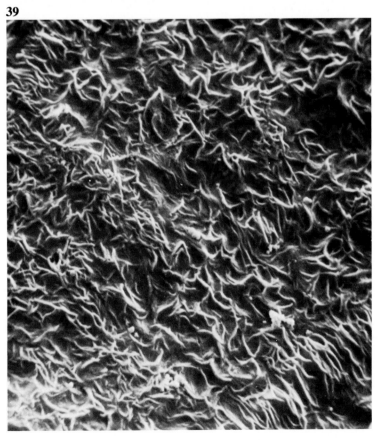

**40, 41.** External surface of the blown HDPE bottle shown in **38** and **39**. The texture of the surface is caused by the inside mould surface and the movement of the polymeric material relative to the mould walls during the blow moulding process (overlapping, cf. the freely exposed internal surface, **38, 39**). (240:1; 2,400:1)

**40**

**41**

**42, 43.** Surface of HDPE film. The photographs clearly show the stretching that has taken place in the direction of haul-off (from bottom left to top right), as well as the cracks that have formed at right angles to that direction.

In this stretched specimen, one can recognise $10-20\mu m$ large zones.

The black, film-like deposits are sticking to the surface and are probably due to the manufacturing process. They are presumably torn parts of a film which was coherent at an earlier stage of the manufacturing process, which have been pulled far apart by the stretching of the base material. (1,000:1; 5,000:1)

42

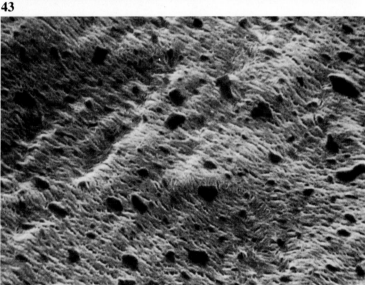

43

**44.** Internal surface of an LDPE film specimen. The stretched surface shows the residues of an originally coherent film, probably originating in deposits in the extrusion die. The individual pieces split off during stretching or were pulled far apart. This can be derived from the shapes of pieces which fit together. (1,000:1)

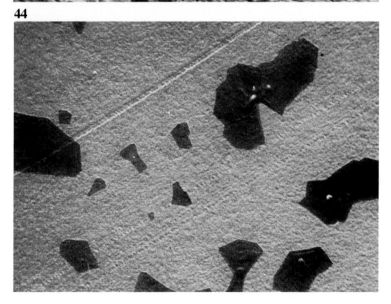

44

## Thermoset surfaces

All thermosets are made from low molecular weight substances which undergo chemical reactions (polymerisation, polycondensation and polyaddition) during processing and thus build up the macromolecular structure. The fine texture of the surfaces is due either to the mould surface finish or – in the case of freely exposed surfaces – to shrinkage or surface tension and textural effects. This also applies to foamed articles produced by the liberation of gas during curing.

**45, 46.** The cavities of a steel structure were filled with polyurethane foam to cut down noise. At the boundary, a 1.5mm thick layer of compact PU was formed (integral structure), which bears the negative impression of the steel surface. (105:1; 1,050:1)

**45**

**46**

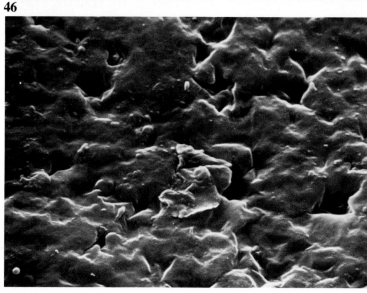

# TEXTURES OF POST-TREATED SURFACES

Polymeric materials can be machined or treated with chemical agents. Machining is normally done with cutting tools which produce various grooved patterns with peak and lip structures (mainly with thermoplastics) or splinter-type structures (mainly with thermosets) (see page 83).

Aggressive chemicals cause surface roughening. The surfaces of welded seams, being freely exposed, have a rounded character.

**47, 48.** Surface of a gas permeable PTFE membrane machined from solid rod. The surface shows the grooves made by the cutting tool as well as lattice-type stretch patterns. The cavities were probably formed due to amorphous-crystalline transformation through considerable local overheating during cutting. (500:1; 10,000:1)

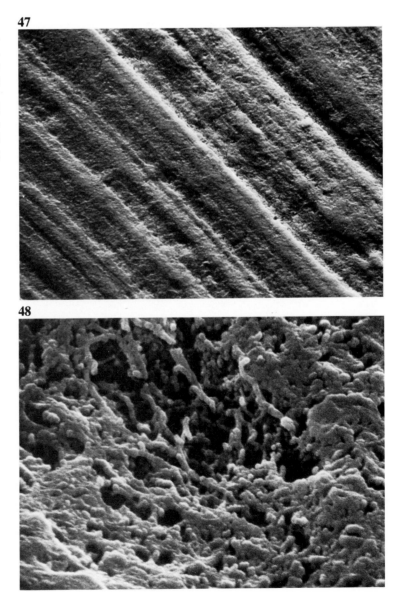

47

48

**49, 50.** EP surface, rubbed down with emery cloth. Surface wear is due to brittle crumbling. (1,200:1; 2,400:1)

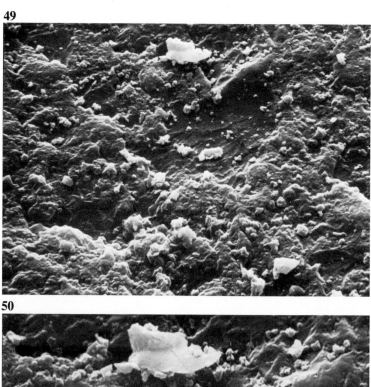

**51.** EP surface, polished with alumina. The deeper indentations were not smoothed out. The rest of the surface shows marks caused by the polishing material. (1,300:1)

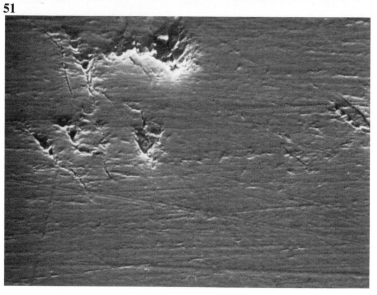

# Faults in the material

Faults in the material may take the form of cavities, inclusions and heterogeneities.

Cavities take the form of holes, bubbles, pores, sink marks etc. Since their surfaces have been freely formed, they are smoother than mechanically damaged surfaces and fracture surfaces.

Foreign bodies in the material become apparent by their particular shape, especially in fracture surfaces. They can be identified by microanalysis.

Inhomogeneities are produced by irregular dispersion of different phases.

We examined a number of specimens and found internal faults to be sources of fractures. This applies to fractures caused by force as well as those caused by vibration. This leads to the conclusion that internal faults are more critical in polymeric materials than they are in metals.

**52.** At a bubble inside a laboratory sample made of POM subjected to vibration, a vibration fracture has started to spread in all directions. (220:1)

**52**

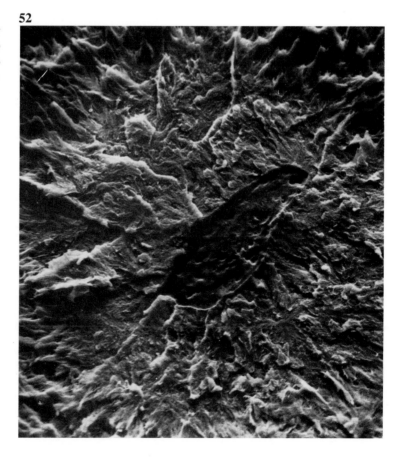

**53.** 4mm diameter shrinkage void in cast nylon (polymerised caprolactam). (50:1)

**54, 55.** 4mm diameter void in cast nylon (polymerised caprolactam) (from **53**). The spherulite boundaries visible in the wall of the cavity indicate that crystallised residual monomer is probably present. (500:1; 2,000:1)

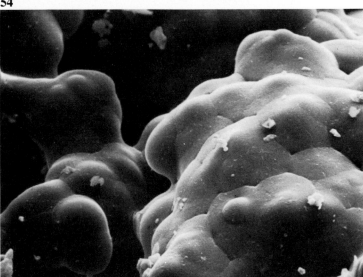

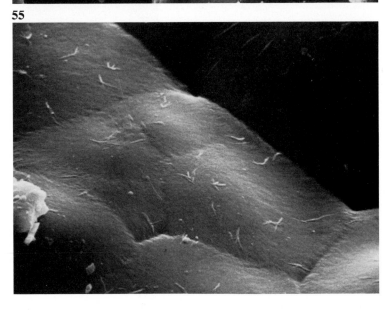

**56, 57.** Hole in PS which was injection moulded at too high a temperature. In the extremely smooth surface of the hole, small foreign bodies have been deposited in micro-craters. (21:1; 5,250:1)

**56**

**57**

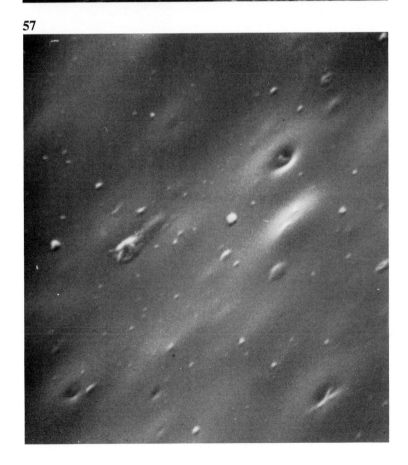

**58–60.** PVC was hot air welded, but the temperature of the air was too high at 470°C. Weld beads were formed on the surface and inside the pores with smooth surfaces, whose fracture surface is shown here. (200:1; 500:1; 2,000:1)

**58**

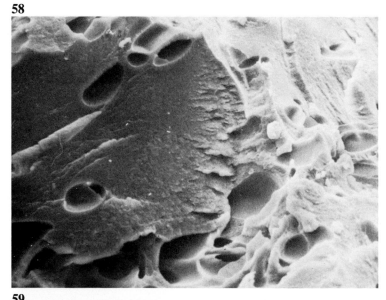

**59**

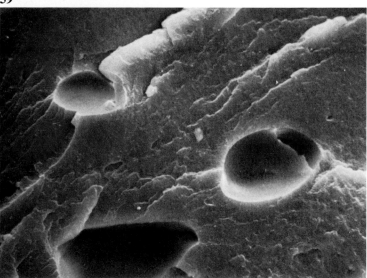

**60**

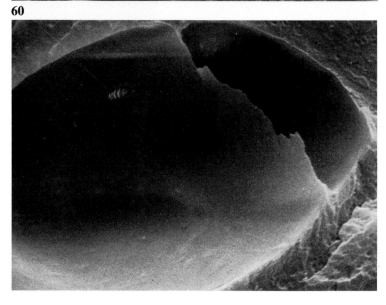

**61–63.** Fracture of POM produced during a creep test in water at 20°C revealed a porous microstructure which was probably produced in the following manner: during solidification the amorphous melt, with a density of 1.05g/cm³, was transformed into an 80% crystalline structure with a density of 1.41g/cm³. This produced an evenly distributed micro-porosity, with few load bearing material bridges. (22:1; 2,200:1; 5,500:1)

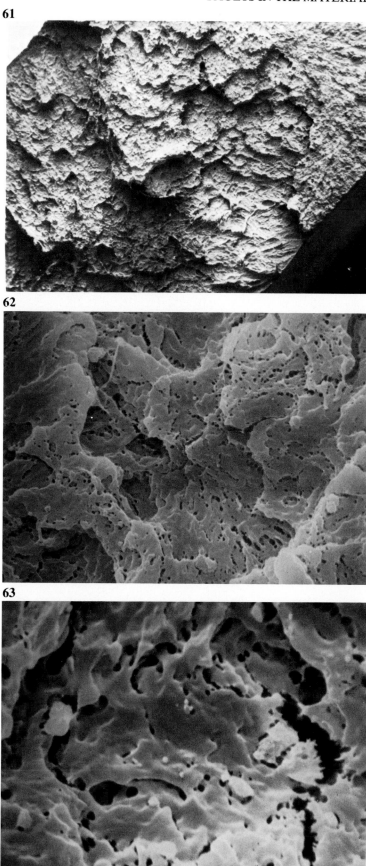

61

62

63

**64**

**64, 65.** A dynamic fatigue fracture propagated from an embedded, calcium-rich foreign body in PA (calcium analysis using electron beam micro-analysis). (100:1; 500:1)

**65**

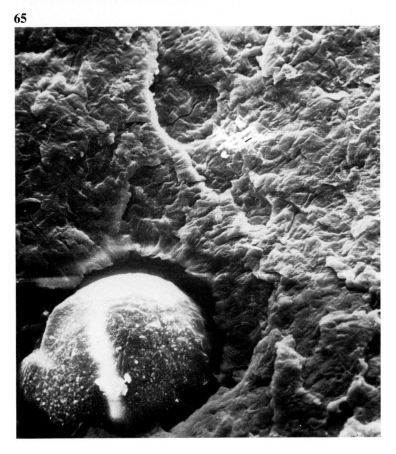

**66.** Embedded calcium stearate in a force fracture of HDPE. (6,000:1)

66

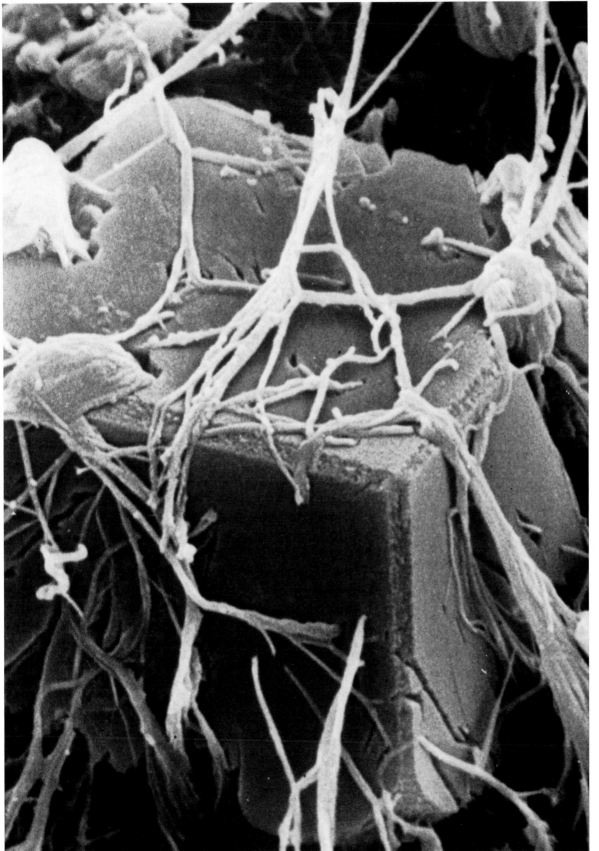

**67, 68.** Creep test on a PE specimen.

A PE pipe, subjected to internal pressure at 80°C fractured after 90 hours. Right round a calcium stearate agglomerate, 120μm in diameter, a surface crack propagated concentrically until it opened up. The force fracture structure can be seen on the left and right hand sides of **67**. The micro-structure of the surface crack consists of long drawn out peaks and fibrils. The slowly propagating surface crack is equivalent in its effect to creep fracture in metals. (22:1; 550:1)

**67**

**68**

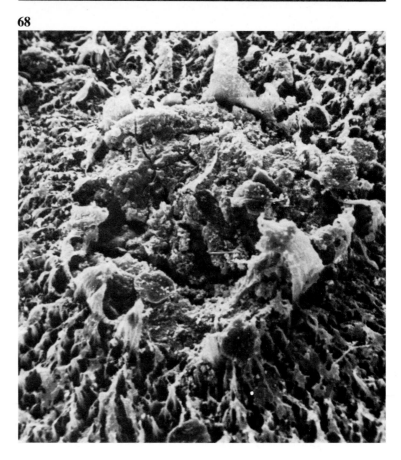

**69, 70.** Hand brake handle made from nylon 66. Cause of force fracture: embedded particles at the boundary between sprue and moulding. Electron beam micro-analysis showed that the particles contained Si, Cl, K and Ca. (120:1; 600:1)

**69**

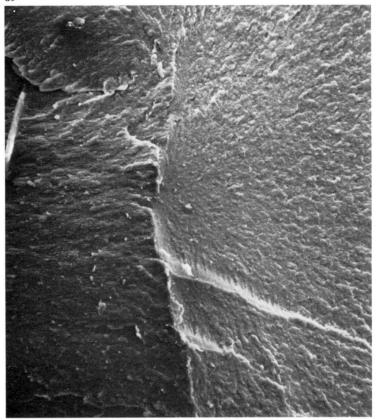

**70**

# 2. Surface damage

When the surface of a polymeric material comes in contact with another solid or medium, the following may occur:

– elastic and visco-elastic (reversible) deformation
– plastic (irreversible) deformation
– abrasive removal of material
– heating due to visco-elastic and plastic deformation (kinetic energy caused by relative movement)
– heating due to heat transfer
– chemical reactions
– diffusion

Elastic deformation leaves no permanent trace on the surfaces. Heat transfer can leave such traces, whilst the other types of interaction will inevitably do so. Whether the damage extends over the entire area or is localised depends on the distribution of destructive occurrences and number per unit area. Uniform wear will take place if the two materials (solid, liquid or gaseous) are in contact over a large surface area. Under practical conditions, multi-phase flows often act on a solid surface, e.g. a flow of liquid with solid particles in it.

A surface may be damaged locally either by a single occurrence or by a concentration of many occurrences at one particular point.

# Mechanical surface damage

Mechanical surface damage is caused not only by solids but also by liquids and gases. Moreover, mechanical damage can occur without direct contact but as a result of external forces attacking the surface from a distance, e.g. constriction.

## WEAR DUE TO FRICTION

**Uniform frictional wear of flat surfaces.** Uniform frictional wear of flat surfaces occurs when two surfaces slide against each other whilst in complete physical contact. We shall first consider the case of dry frictional wear, i.e. in the absence of lubricant. It must be remembered that no surface is completely smooth when seen through the microscope – there is always a certain amount of roughness. When two surfaces are pressed together lightly for the first time they are in physical contact only at a few raised points and ridges. As soon as the two surfaces start to move in relation to each other, the raised peaks of one surface will move laterally against those of the other. The weaker, i.e. more easily deformed surface gives way and is dragged along in the direction of movement. This results in the formation of lips, peaks and fibrils (**71**), which are eventually torn off and roll between the two surfaces. In the case of filled polymeric materials, filler particles are released from the polymer under these conditions. Being granular,

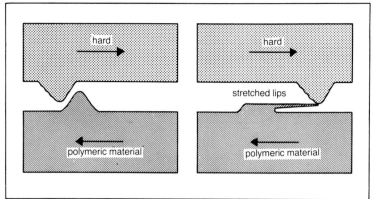

**71.** Dry frictional wear of polymeric material due to stretching of raised peaks with the formation of lips, peaks or fibrils which ultimately tear off and roll between the two surfaces.

they can accelerate wear between the two surfaces. If the movement is rotary or alternating, with a fixed path, a pattern of grooves will be created on the polymer surface.

If polymer rubs against polymer, e.g. in gears, the flexibility (low modulus of elasticity) of the teeth often results in a larger contact surface and therefore deformation is spread over a larger area than in the case of metal/metal contact. A wavy pattern is often produced by the many small-area extensions which take place successively. Abrasive wear continues as long as the surfaces are under pressure. Movement between two surfaces need not necessarily be in the same direction to cause millimetre deep wear – the movement can also be oscillating.

At increased pressures or increased sliding speeds, frictional heat increases wear. At first there is merely local softening, leading to momentary welding, followed by separation. The result is repeated passing of material between the two surfaces. This process usually occurs when two similar polymeric materials with similar softening points rub against each other. This type of wear can ultimately lead to seizing up and thus to failure of the component. The wear processes described above can be much reduced if a film of lubricant prevents direct contact, partly or completely, between the friction partners. During the initial stages, however, raised peaks will always be flattened out first, as described, and after a while this process is complete.

Wear is particularly marked if foreign particles or fragments such as swarf or mineral dust get in between the two sliding surfaces. This type of wear is illustrated in **72**. The hard particles act like small tools. This becomes apparent if one looks at the crystalline particles contained in normal dust through the scanning electron microscope (**73**). The shape and size of these particles have a decisive effect on the rate of wear. In wear caused by particles, the roughness of the worn surface is not directly related to the rate of wear or abrasion.

*Rate of wear (abrasion)*
The rate of wear increases with the size and hardness of the particle, and also depends on the character of its edges. This applies to all types of particles.

The influence exerted by the opposing surface is not so easy to determine. If it is hard, e.g. porcelain, the foreign particles cannot get a foothold. If, on the other hand, it is soft, the particles are embedded in it and remain there (**72** and **104**). In this way the cutting force of all shapes of particles is increased. The effective cutting depth, on the other hand, is increased in the case of platelet-type particles (spreading effect), but

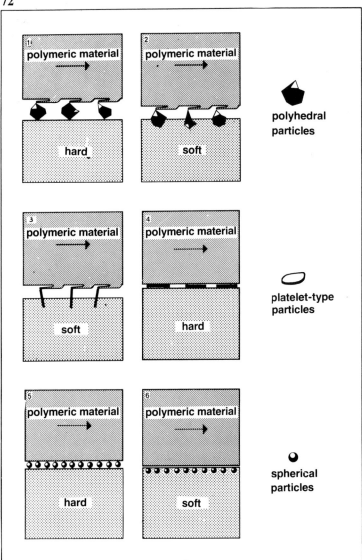

**72.** Abrasive wear of polymeric material due to presence of foreign particles. The rate of abrasion decreases from example 1 to example 6, assuming the foreign body to have the same hardness. The rate of abrasion will alter if the particle hardness changes. The wear on the surface of the lower member has not been taken into account. Porcelain= hard, polymer=soft.

decreased in the case of polyhedral and spherical particles. From this it follows that platelet-type particles will always cause more abrasion with a soft opposing surface than with a hard one (about ten times as much).

Polyhedral and spherical particles sometimes follow this rule. Mostly, however, the reduction of cutting depth due to the soft opposing surface is the determining factor so that there is less abrasion with a soft opposing surface than with a hard one.

*Roughness of worn surfaces*

Surface roughness increases with size and hardness and with the number of edges of the foreign particles, as well as with the hardness of the opposing surface. Particles are not retained by a hard opposing surface but execute tumbling movements and thus produce torn, fibrous, rough wear structures. Soft surfaces, on the other hand, will hold on to the particles, whose effective cutting depth, except in the case of platelets, is thus reduced. This results in largely parallel grooves which are quite shallow, i.e. a smooth worn surface is produced (polishing effect, cf. soft cloth and polish).

In the case of fibre reinforced materials, wear is borne mainly by the hard fibres. This is possible only if the fibres are deeply and firmly anchored in the material. Fibres lying parallel to the surface exposed to wear tend to break off after a short while and act as foreign particles in that they promote wear. These glass particles cause wear of the glass fibre reinforced polymeric material against steel. They act on steel in two ways:

1. The steel matrix is plastically deformed, and tongue-like projections are formed, which ultimately break off and act as foreign particles.

2. Hard phases in the steel surface (carbide) remain as a relief structure and attack the polymer, which now wears away rapidly.

**73**

**73.** Particles of ordinary dust. The largest particle has brittle fracture surfaces and sharp edges which can act like tiny cutting tools between two surfaces rubbing against each other. (2,000:1)

**74, 75.** Dry running caused a PBTP tooth flank to wear away by about 0.5mm. In the worn area one can see large, stretched zones (see **76** and **77**). In the top left-hand corner of **75** peaks and lips have formed (see **78** and **79**). Abraded particles (see **80** and **81**) have collected in the deep eruption (**74**). (20:1; 100:1)

**74**

**75**

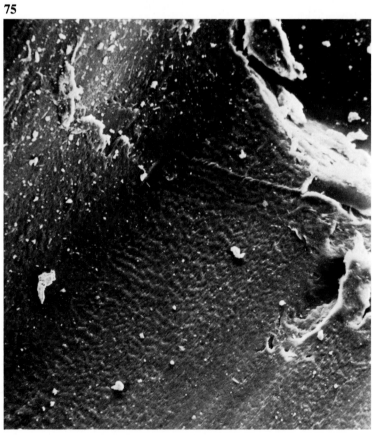

**76, 77.** Surface layer of a PBTP tooth flank (from **75**), stretched by shear forces, after dry running. The opposing surface moved from bottom left to top right. Material displacements occurred in that direction and the channels produced are bridged by fibrils. (500:1; 2,000:1)

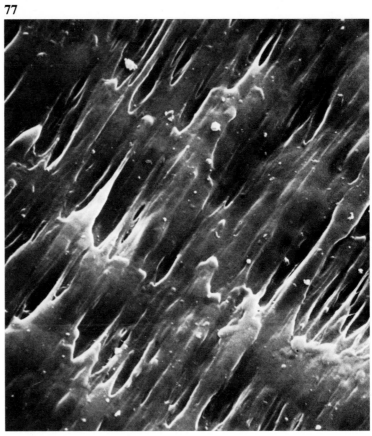

**78, 79.** Peak structures at the torn-off ends of stretched portions in a PBTP tooth flank after dry running (from **75**). (500:1; 2,000:1)

**78**

**79**

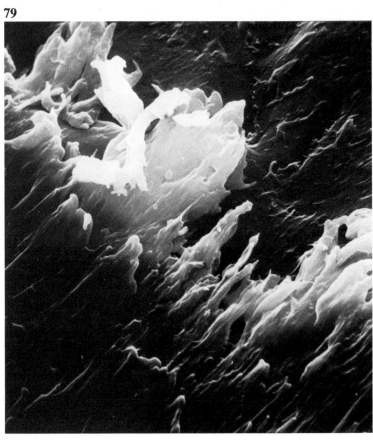

**80, 81.** Abraded particles from a worn PBTP tooth flank after dry running (from **74**). These particles consist of torn-off, rolled up lips which were torn out of the surface at temperatures far below the melting point. (2,000:1; 2,000:1)

**80**

**81**

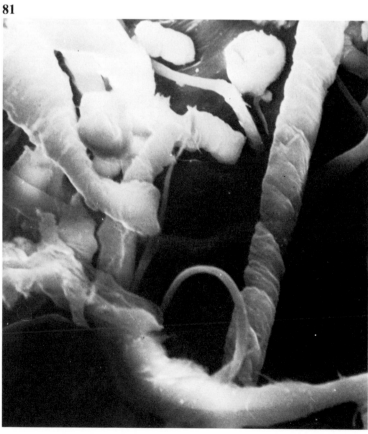

**82.** Frictional wear of a bushing made of PA 66 with 8% HDPE rubbing against a shaft made of steel 1.5Ni. On the left of the picture one can see a wide smear of softened polymer. The small bulges on the right are presumably due to molten HDPE (melting point 140°C). PA 66 on the other hand melts only at 250°C. (20:1)

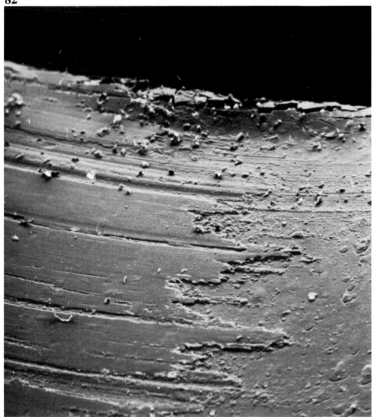

**83.** Rounded shapes and shrinkage cracks prove that a PE particle enriched with iron (as shown by microanalysis) had melted. (5,000:1)

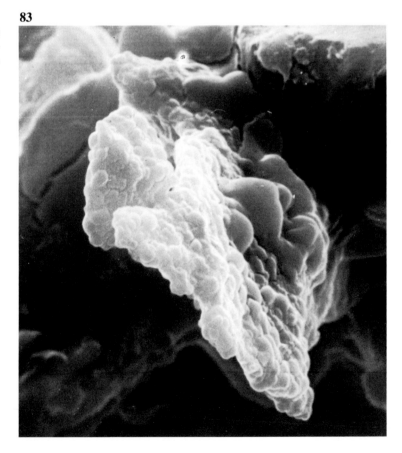

**84.** Abraded particle, rich in iron, on the worn surface of a bushing made of PA 66 with 8% HDPE which had rubbed against a 1.5Ni steel shaft. (2,000:1)

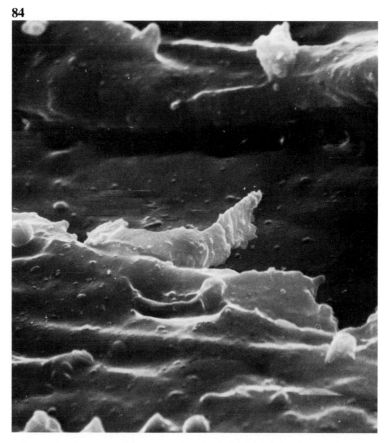

**85.** Iron distribution in material shown in **84**. (2,000:1)

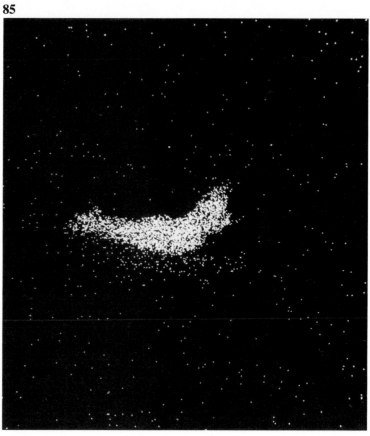

**86.** Frictional wear of a bushing made of PA 66 with 8% HDPE which had rubbed against a steel shaft. In the top right-hand corner of the picture one can see a smear of softened polymer. The many small bulges are probably due to molten HDPE (140°C). PA on the other hand melts only at about 250°C. (55:1)

**87.** Bulge caused by high temperature, partly surrounded by channels. The alignment of the bulge possibly depends on the injection direction at right angles to the direction of movement. (1,100:1)

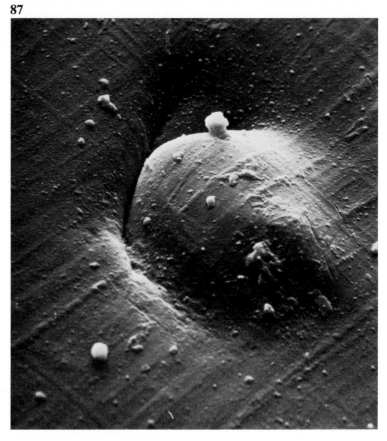

**88, 89.** Frictional wear of a bushing made of PA 66 with 8% HDPE rubbing against a steel shaft. Softened polymer has been smeared across the surface and formed droplets which prove the existence of a melted intermediate phase. (220:1; 1,100:1)

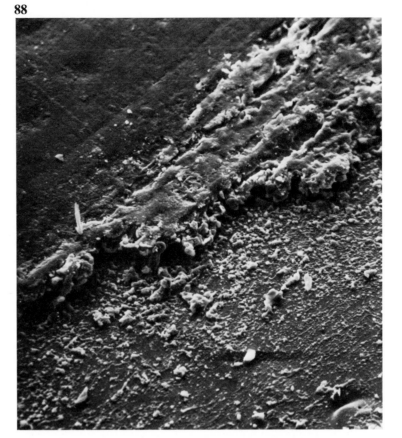

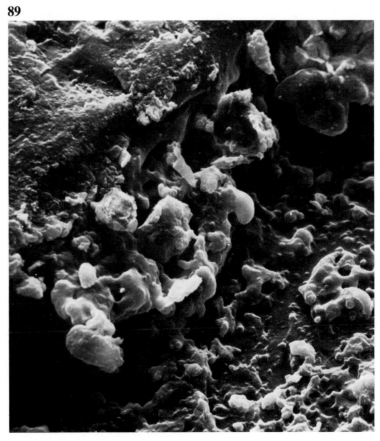

**90, 91.** Tooth of a coupling with convex profile teeth made of PA 66 was connected to a steel clutch. High pressure all over the surface led to large amounts of material being removed, as shown by the super-imposed layers (**91**). (19:1; 200:1)

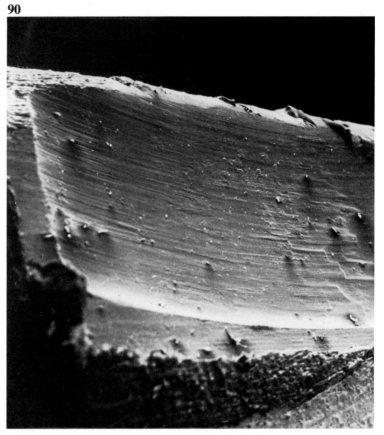

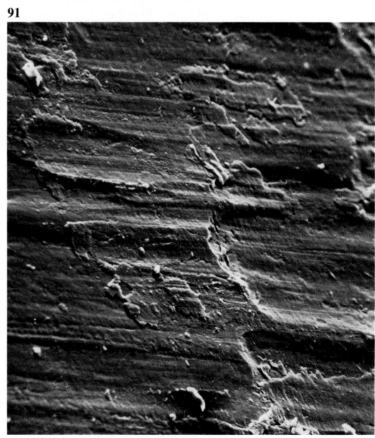

**92, 93.** Signs of fracture in the shape of peaks and fibrils can be seen near the edges of the smeared surfaces. This proves fusion at high temperatures, followed by tearing off. The requirement was that the polymer adhered to the opposing steel surface. (1,000:1; 5,000:1)

**92**

**93**

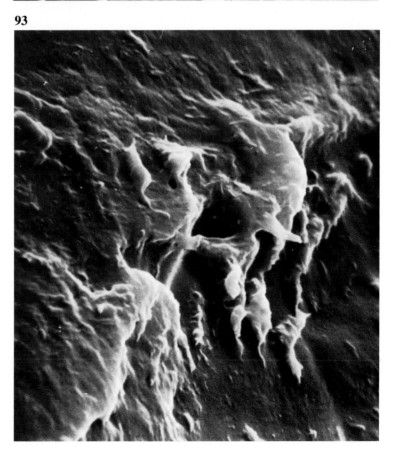

**94, 95.** A steel shaft was run in an anti-friction bearing made of PA 66 with 8% HDPE. The movement of one against the other caused raised areas between the grooves, made in the polymer by turning, to be smoothed out. Since no traces of melted material are to be seen at the edges of the load bearing surfaces, this smoothing out must have been caused by abrasive wear. Fine iron oxide particles acted as an abrasive polish, producing a smooth surface. Note the bulges in **94**, which are due to high temperatures. (110:1; 1,100:1)

**94**

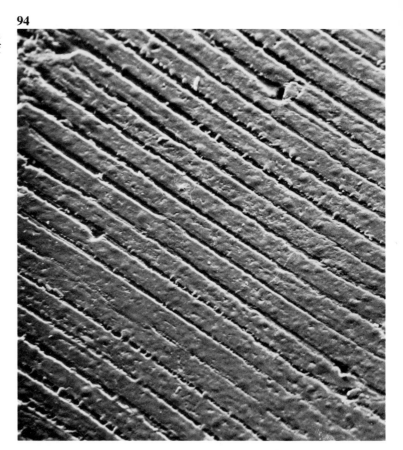

**95**

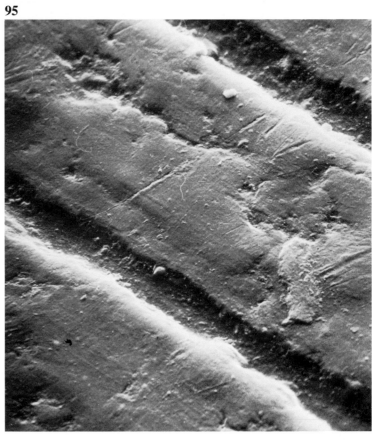

**96, 97.** The sliding surface has been coloured brown by excessive temperatures during dry running (from **94**). This brown colour is due to iron oxides present as finely distributed particles on the sliding surface. A larger particle can be seen in the iron distribution picture (**97**). (1,100:1; 1,100:1)

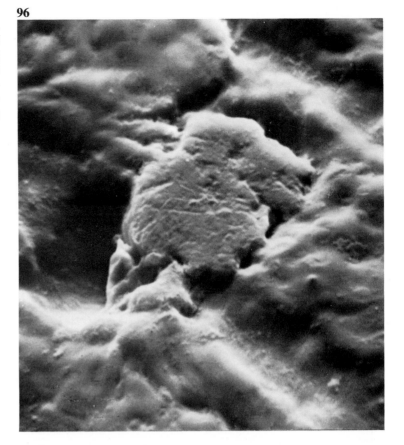

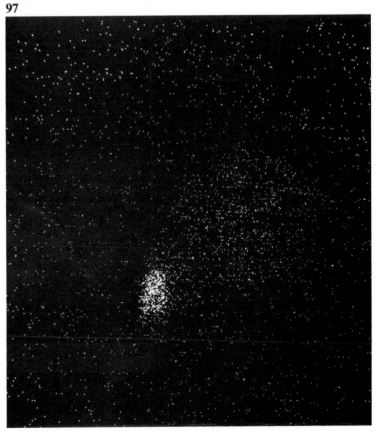

**98, 99.** Frictional wear of an HDPE specimen against steel in a laboratory test.

The rotary movement of the hard steel specimen against the polymeric material has stretched the raised parts in the direction of movement, forming peaks, fibrils or lips and grooves. (22:1; 2,200:1)

**98**

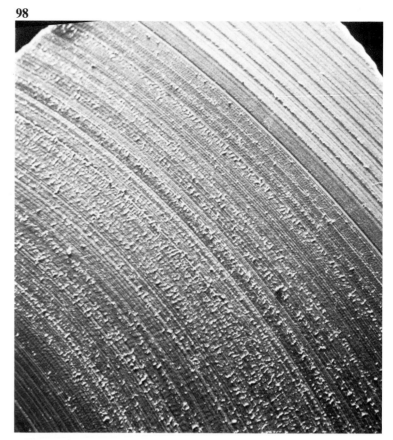

**99**

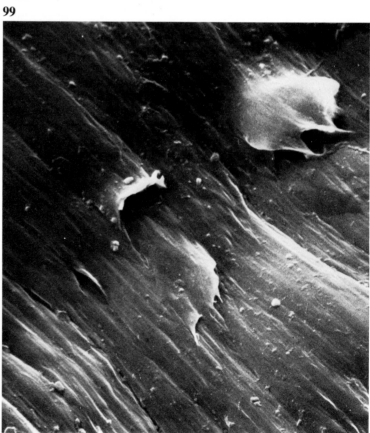

**100, 101.** Frictional wear of a POM specimen rubbing against PETP in a laboratory test.

The rotary movement caused peaks and grooves to form. The granular deposits on the surface are probably NaCl crystals originating from physiological salt solution. (20:1; 2,000:1)

**100**

**101**

**102–104.** Plasticised PVC surface which had rubbed against a PETP sieve, with kaolin particles in between. A number of these have become embedded in the soft PVC surface and protrude as tiny cutting tools. (55:1; 5,500:1; 11,000:1)

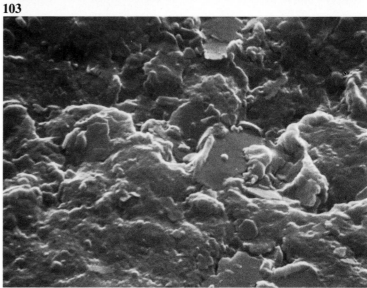

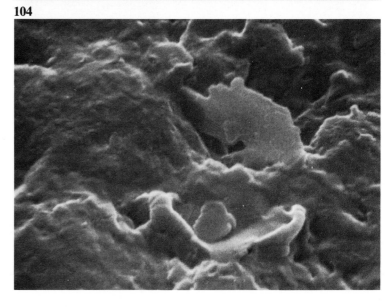

**105, 106.** Abrasive wear of a PETP sieve which had rubbed against porcelain, with talc particles in between. The platelet-like particles were unable to become embedded in the hard porcelain surface and thus produced a fibrous, rough surface on the PETP sieve. (52:1; 1,050:1)

**105**

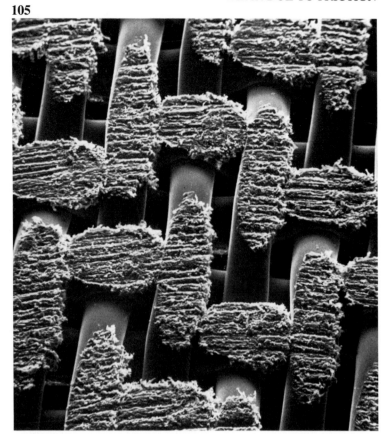

**106**

**107, 108.** Abrasive wear of a PETP sieve which had rubbed against porcelain, with calcium carbonate particles with coccolith shells in between. These coarse particles were unable to become embedded in the hard porcelain surface and thus produced a rough, fibrous surface on the PETP sieve. (55:1; 2,200:1)

107

108

**109, 110.** Abrasive wear of a PETP sieve which had rubbed against PVC, with calcium carbonate particles in between. These particles were partly with sharp edges, partly spherical. They were forced into the soft PVC surface where they acted like tiny cutting tools (**72**). In this way, very smooth wear was produced on the surface, with parallel micro-grooves (polishing effect). (55:1; 2,200:1)

**109**

**110**

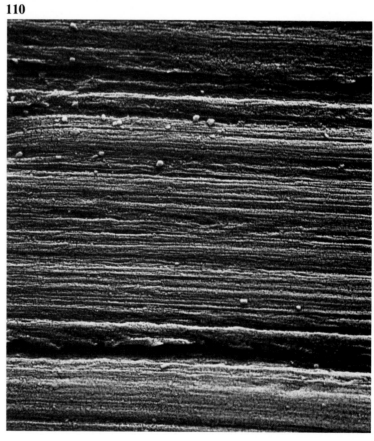

**111, 112.** Carbon fibre reinforced epoxy resin was rubbed against steel in a laboratory test (material for artificial limbs, intermediate medium physiological NaCl solution). During this test, a thin film was formed which tore off only at the transversely oriented carbon fibres. (650:1; 2,600:1)

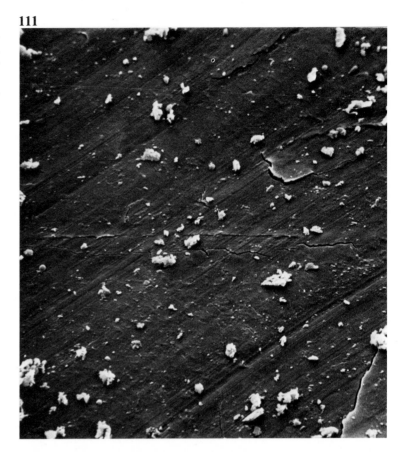

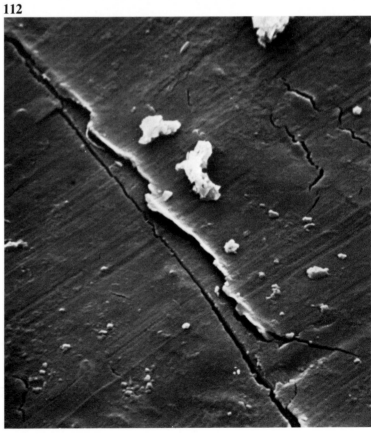

**113, 114.** Frictional wear of carbon fibre reinforced epoxy resin rubbing against a cobalt based alloy used for artificial hip joints. Intermediate medium: physiological NaCl solution. Wear is reduced by the presence of carbon fibres, which must be deeply embedded in the material. Fibres lying parallel to the surface being abraded soon become detached. (1,200:1; 1,200:1)

113

114

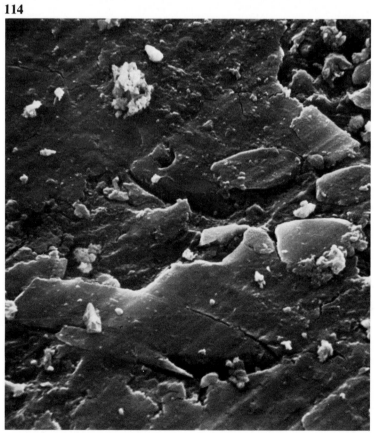

**115, 116.** Frictional wear of brittle epoxy resin against a cobalt based alloy used for artificial hip joints (laboratory tests). Intermediate medium: physiological NaCl solution. Wear is due to two kinds of mechanism:

1. Brittle, conchoidal crumbling where the sharp-edged fragments act as foreign particles.

2. Very fine abrasion, with particles measuring less than 1μm, which agglomerate to form flattened-out deposits. (115:1; 2,200:1)

**115**

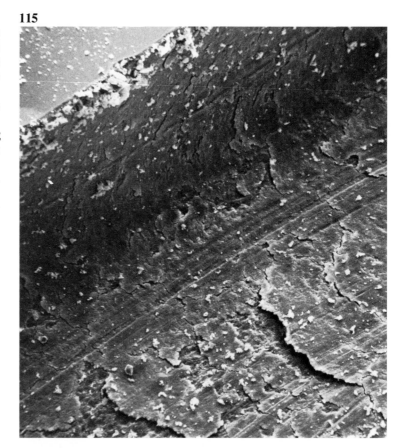

**116**

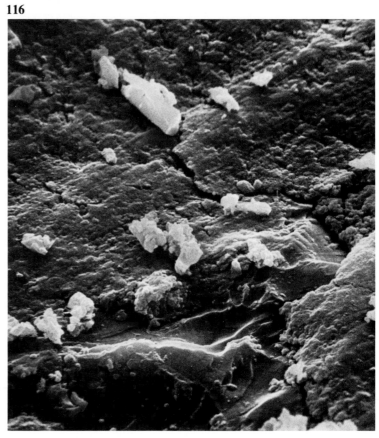

**117, 118.** Wall of a compartment of a bearing cage, made from glass fibre reinforced PTFE. The frictional wear applies mainly to the glass fibres. PTFE was deposited on the glass fibre surfaces and was found to have good adhesion. (700:1; 2,800:1)

**117**

**118**

75

**Local frictional wear (pitting).** A common type of wear, referred to as pitting, occurs on lubricated flanks of teeth. The small arrows in **119** indicate the direction of sliding displacement of a driven and of a driving tooth. The material of the tooth flank surface is stretched in the direction of these arrows. During this process, stretched lips a few mm long are formed in places, and below them flat fissures. These can give rise to dynamic fatigue cracks if the material is subjected to alternating loads. The direction in which these cracks spread is indicated by a wavy line in **120**.

The main direction of crack propagation coincides with the direction of migration D of the stressed points on the tooth flanks. Finally, parts of the flakes undermined by the dynamic fatigue fracture break off and leave behind tiny holes or pits (hence the name pitting). If the stressed tooth flanks are of equal strength, pitting occurs most frequently at the base of the teeth of the driving wheel (b in **119**). If the driven wheel is made of low strength material, pitting will normally occur at the base of the teeth of that wheel. Pitting occurs very rarely at points a and d. Points b and c, which are the most likely points to be damaged, have in common that the stressed points of contact extend from the ends of the lips to their bases (negative slip). Dynamic fatigue fractures in an area where there is pitting can penetrate so deeply into the material that they cause the teeth to break.

Pitting does not occur under conditions of dry running where there is a high degree of abrasive wear. In this instance the flanks become worn through abrasion so that the contact pattern changes. This again leads to fatigue fractures because of excessive movement stress, resulting in penetration of the cross-section of the tooth. Polymer gear wheels are often used (at low stress) without lubrication.

**119**

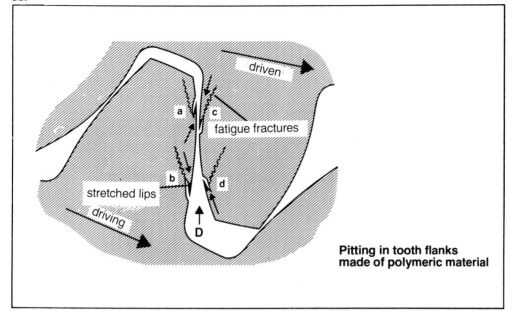

**Pitting in tooth flanks
made of polymeric material**

**120**

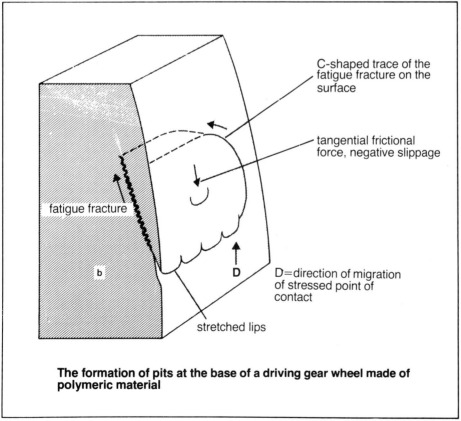

**The formation of pits at the base of a driving gear wheel made of
polymeric material**

**121**

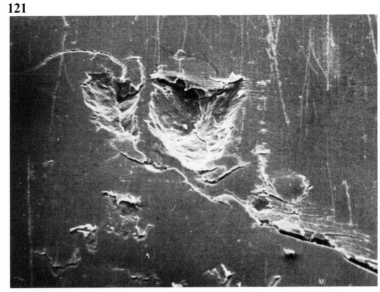

**121, 122.** Pitting on the tooth flank of a driving, oil lubricated gear wheel made of PA 66. Direction of frictional wear from top to bottom. Propagation of vibration cracks from bottom to top, recognisable from the C-shape of the crack along the surface. (100:1; 500:1)

**122**

**123.** Pitting on the tooth flank of a gear wheel made of PA 66. Direction of frictional wear from top to bottom. Propagation of vibration cracks from bottom to top. The fatigue fractures spreading below the surface are traced on the surface as cracks shaped like pliers. (1,050:1)

**123**

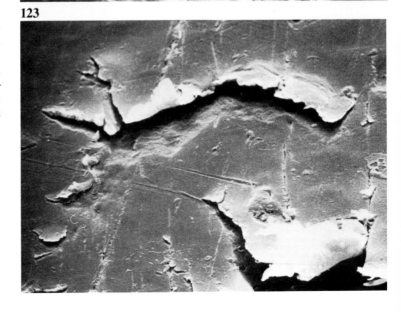

# WEAR DUE TO ROLLERS

Roller bearings made from polymeric materials are little used in engineering. Only bearings made with POM sockets and steel balls have achieved importance in furniture manufacture because of their silent operation. Furthermore, ball bearings entirely made from polymeric materials are used for operations in corrosive media. As with steel balls, pitting may occur here, too. The material may melt at high operating temperatures.

The processes which take place during the operation of rollers and ball bearings resemble those encountered in frictional wear. The changing stresses produce fatigue cracks which originate on the surface and which ultimately cause pitting. Similarly, surfaces may be heated by friction, with the associated occurrences such as softening and melting, coupled with increased wear.

At high stresses (Hertzian compression), polymeric materials may also be damaged by the high temperatures developed – which may even lead to melting of the material – at the point where there are maximum shear stresses. Since this point is very much lower underneath the contact surface in polymeric materials (because of their much lower modulus of elasticity) than in steel, this does not cause direct damage to the surface.

**124.** Wear caused by rolling in a roller made of PUR elastomer. (100:1)

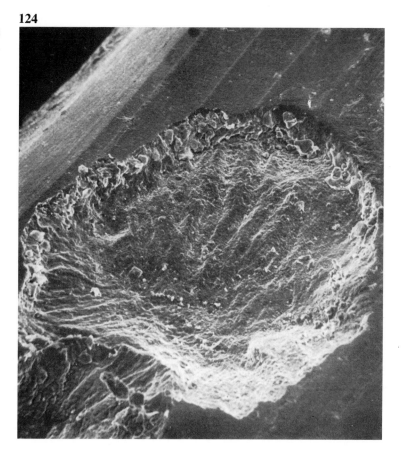

124

**125.** Dynamic fatigue cracks which originated from stretched, tongue-like projections (from **124**, bottom left). (1,100:1)

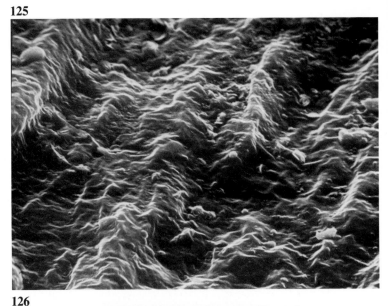
125

126

**126, 127.** Wear caused by rolling, in a POM ring inside a ball bearing after dry running at room temperature.

The alternating stresses produced by the steel balls caused pincer-like vibration cracks to spread, originating from the stretched, tongue-like projections. The damage mechanism is analogous to pitting at the tooth flanks (**120**). The actual cause of the damage was excessive alternating stress and sliding movement between the two surfaces. (20:1; 50:1)

127

**128, 129.** Wear caused by rolling in a POM roller, diameter 80mm, which rotated against a steel roll in a laboratory test. The wavy pattern is due to softening of the surface. (120:1; 600:1)

**128**

**129**

**130, 131.** Wear caused by rolling, in a POM ring inside a ball bearing after dry running at room temperature.

The alternating stresses produce heat, which causes local softening of the material below the surface (cf. **380**). The additional mechanical compressive deformation by the rolling steel balls causes a wavy pattern to be formed. (210:1; 1,000:1)

**130**

**131**

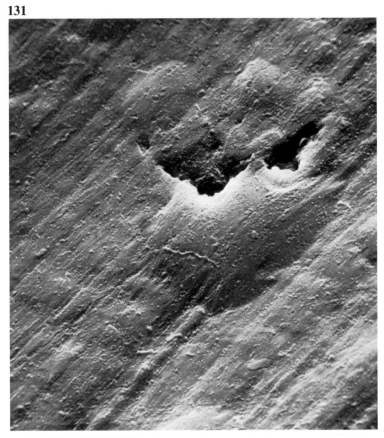

# LOCALISED, MECHANICAL SURFACE DAMAGE

Localised, mechanical surface damage can occur during manufacture, transport, assembly or operation, due to the action of foreign bodies. In stressed machine components these damaged areas are frequently the starting points for all kinds of cracks. Other possible effects are disturbance of the flow of liquids passing over the damaged surface, as well as visible impairment (reduction of gloss, cloudiness). Mechanical damage also includes marks left by machining. These marks penetrate the natural surface of a specimen and distort the microstructure. Force fracture structures are to be expected in the micro-region.

**132, 133.** Section cut through an ABS specimen. The knife blade cutting from bottom right to top left made a pattern of grooves and peak structures on the surface. The recovery of stretched fibrils when the two halves were pulled apart caused thickening to take place at the end of the peaks. (500:1; 2,000:1)

**132**

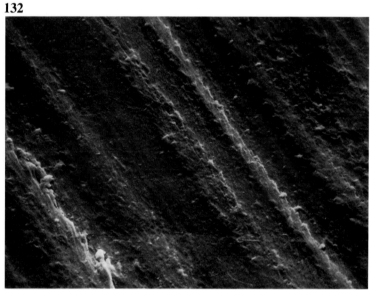

**133**

**134, 135.** Mechanical damage to a SAN surface, made by a pin. Traces of ductile fracture can be seen in the scratch. (50:1; 500:1)

**134**

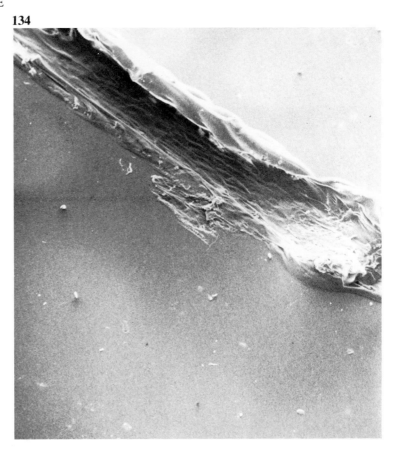

**135**

**136, 137.** Rounded grooves were produced by turning a PVC shaft. A characteristic feature is the ductile stretching of fibrils with thickened ends, and the parallel alignment of accumulations of material along the groove walls. (200:1; 1,000:1)

**136**

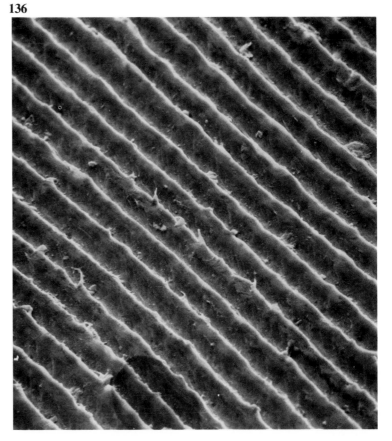

**137**

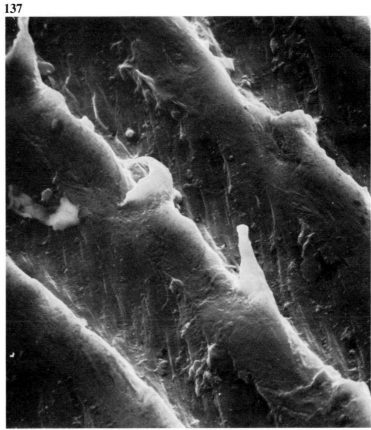

**138, 139.** Rough-turning of a PVC shaft produced deep, V-shaped grooves with deformation structures along the walls. These consist of wide, oblique material accumulations (similar to **137**) and fine striped patterns at right angles to these. This is a flow zone pattern. The thick shavings were unable to escape through compression and had, therefore, to move upwards. A peak-like, fibrillar fracture pattern was formed along the rims of the grooves. (210:1; 1,050:1)

**138**

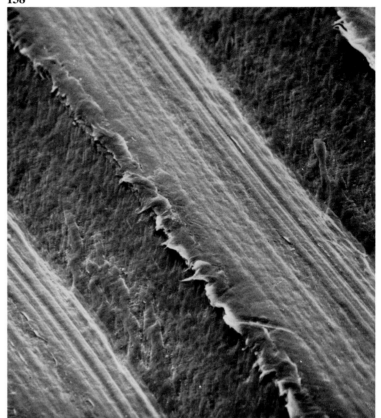

**139**

**140, 141.** Smooth turning of a PVC shaft produced shallow V-shaped grooves. The swarf was able to escape upwards without difficulty. Here, too, flow lines can be distinguished along the sides of the grooves (bottom left) (cf. **139**). (210:1; 1,050:1)

**140**

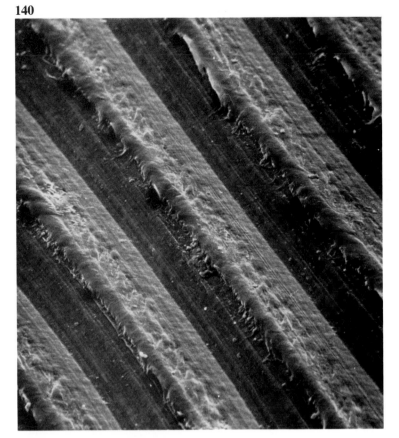

**141**

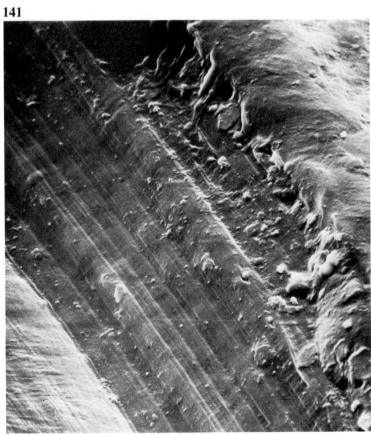

**142.** A cut through a tube, made from viscose fibres, using a sharp knife, produced shear surfaces transversely across the individual fibres, with grooves and lips where the knife blade issued. (600:1)

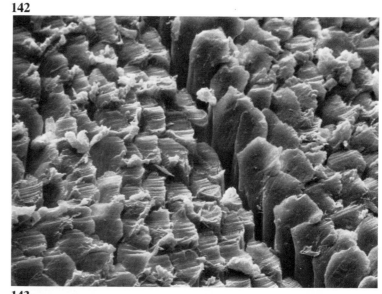

**143.** A cut through the viscose fibres enveloping a tube, using a blunt knife, separated the individual fibres by squeezing and pulling them. The deformed fibre ends are clearly distinguishable from the ends of fibres which had been cut with a sharp knife. (550:1)

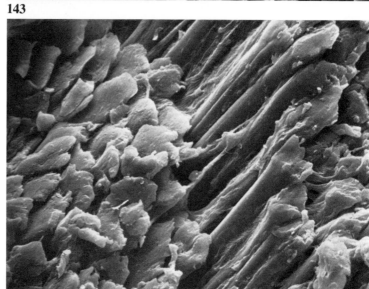

**144.** Viscose fibres of a tube, which had been damaged by a saw. Stretching produced by the blunt instrument formed frayed edges. (650:1)

**145, 146.** Surface of an extruded and then ground PC rod. The characteristic features of material removal are lips and peaks oriented in the direction of machining. There are some isolated particles of abrasive in the polymer surface. (540:1; 2,200:1)

**145**

**146**

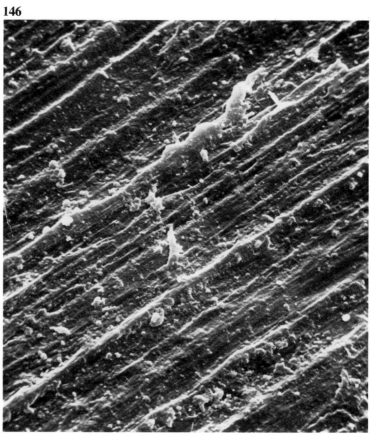

**147**

**147, 148.** The mark made by a hammer blow on a PVC surface. The mark can be divided into cracking, indentation and compression zones. (26:1; 620:1)

Crack zone at the end of an oblique hammer blow, with the characteristic stretched peaks (from **147**).

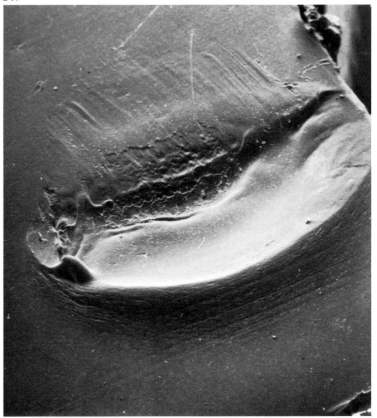

**148**

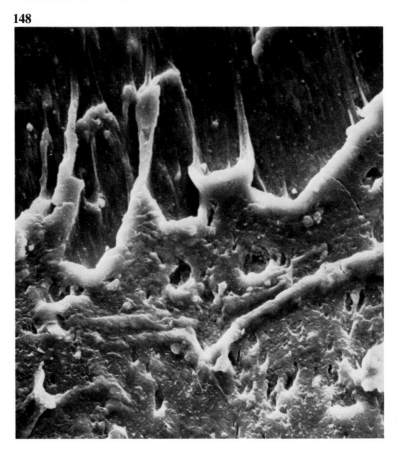

**149, 150.** Oblique hammer blow in a PVC surface (from **147**). The area where the hammer slid tangentially under pressure is characterised by foreign particles having been torn out (cf. ball indentation, **154**). (2,600:1; 1,300:1)

Compression zone at the lowest point of a hammer blow (from **147**). A notable feature is the cracks between the compressive creases.

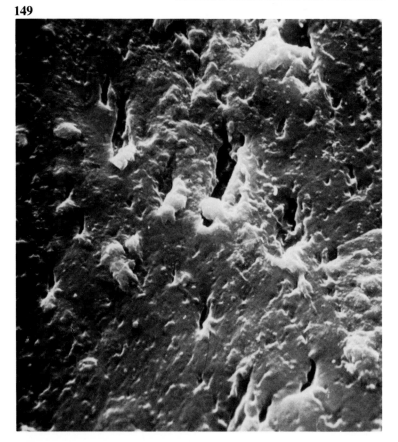

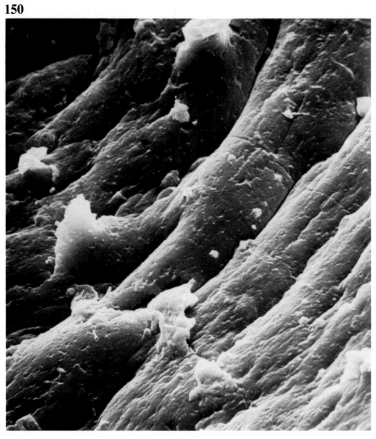

**151.** A bead was formed at the end outside an oblique hammer blow on a PVC surface. (65:1; 1,300:1)

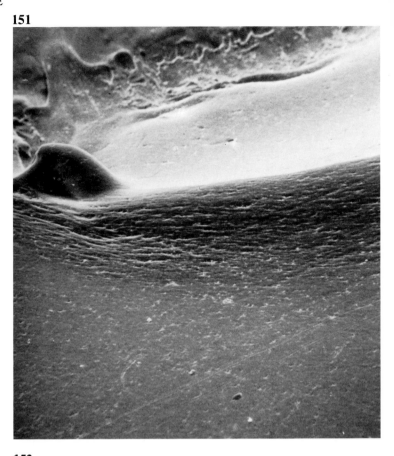

**152.** Note the cracks between the compressive creases (from **151**). (1,300:1)

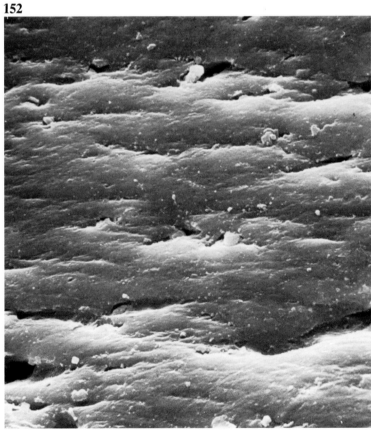

**153.** Ball indentation in the surface of a PVC sheet. (60:1)

**154.** Area of great compression at the centre of the ball indentation (from **153**). The flow in the polymer along the ball has caused filler particles to be exposed on the surface. (6,000:1)

**155.** Normal surface outside the indentation, where the filler particles are completely enveloped by the PVC. (6,000:1)

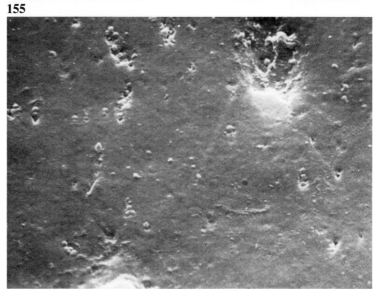

# WEAR DUE TO BOMBARDMENT WITH SOLID PARTICLES

In process technology and conveying operations it is often necessary to transport or separate streams of solid particles. The materials used for this purpose are subject to heavy wear caused by their bombardment with these particles. Here one distinguishes between vertical and tangential streams. The impinging particles cause elastic and plastic deformation of polymeric materials. As the foreign particle penetrates the polymer it stretches it. Material is worn away or abraded due to lips and fibrils, which result from the stretching, being torn off (156). Brittle materials splinter when subjected to this kind of particle bombardment.

Deformable polymers and rubbers are generally more resistant to this type of wear than metals because they have more elastic deformability (effect of a fishing net).

**156**

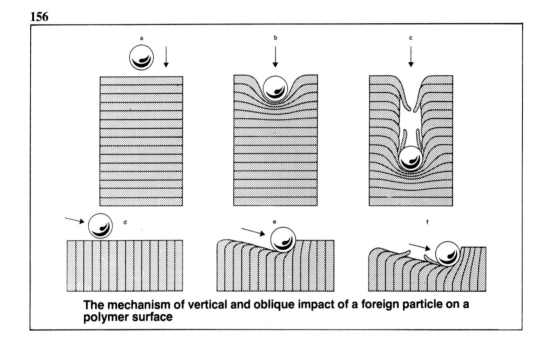

**The mechanism of vertical and oblique impact of a foreign particle on a polymer surface**

**157, 158.** Wear due to solid particle bombardment in high molecular weight HDPE. Impact of sand used for making chill casting moulds at an angle of 45° and a velocity of 40m/s stretches the material until it tears. Lips and fibrils, linked or separated at one end and greatly stretched, are the characteristic features of this type of damage.

At the top left-hand corner of the photograph one can see where a particle, travelling tangentially from bottom right, has formed a bead.

At the centre of **158** a loop, stretched as in a fishing net, can be seen. Its two ends are still linked to the base material. (550:1; 220:1)

**157**

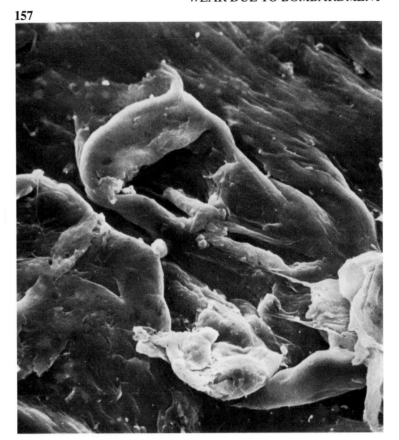

**158**

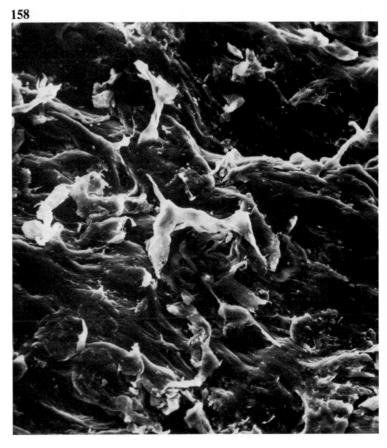

# IMPINGEMENT OF DROPLETS

The effect of high speed bombardment of polymeric materials by droplets of water is similar to wear due to bombardment with solid particles. The characteristic features are:

*Definite lips, peaks and stretched areas in the case of ductile thermoplastics. Slight plastic deformation and brittle fractures in the case of amorphous thermoplastics and elastomers.*

*Areas of dynamic fatigue fractures due to numerous successive droplet impingements.*

The speed of the impinging particles is important. As explained on pages 12–14, the ductility decreases as the rate of loading increases. We shall now show how a material behaves when subjected to high speed stressing.

**159**

**159, 160.** The vertical impact of droplets of water on PE, at a velocity of 400m/s, frays the material which is worn down by very fine fibre ends being torn off. This is an example of a highly extensible, semi-crystalline thermoplastic material. (22:1; 1,400:1)

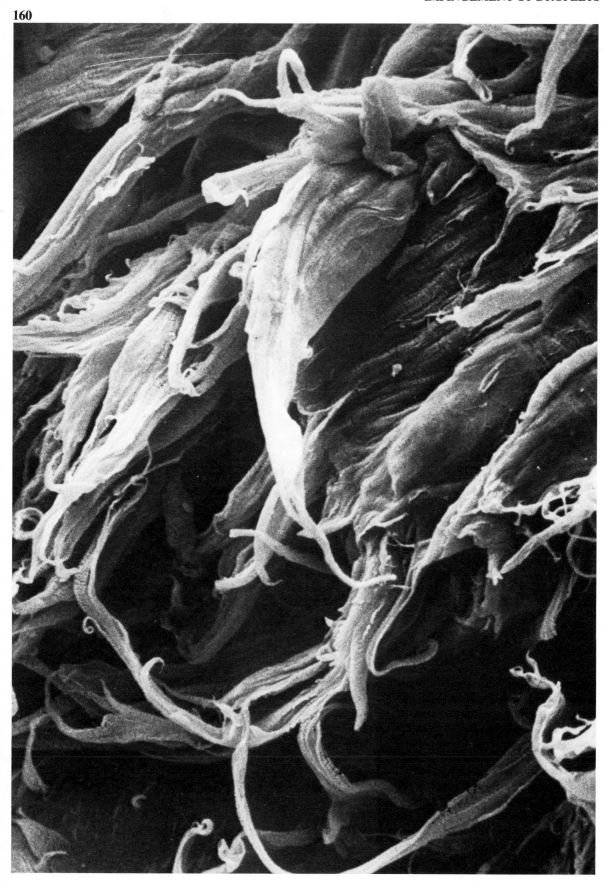

**161, 162.** Droplet impact on a PU elastomer surface.

The impact of drops of water at a velocity of 400m/s produced alternating stresses in the polymer. These led to numerous vibration cracks. The paths taken by these cracks and their front portions can be seen in **162**. This is an example of an elastomer with little extensibility. (18:1; 500:1)

161

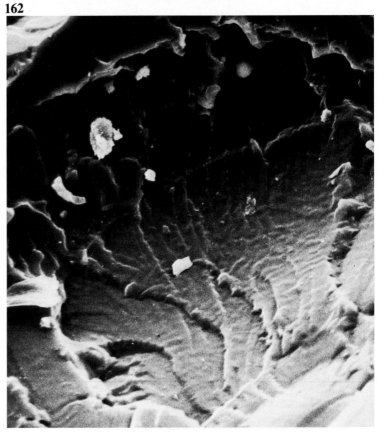

162

**163, 164.** The impact of drops of water at a velocity of 400m/s produced vibrations in the PU elastomer. The resultant fatigue cracks extend from top left to bottom right. In this direction there are vibration crack paths, some of which have assumed a ramp form and which here and there show transverse striations (especially in **163**, top left). (500:1; 1,000:1)

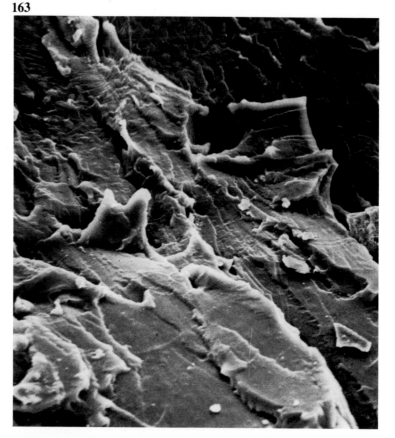

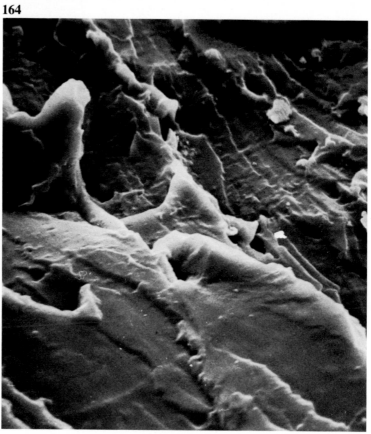

**165–167.** The vertical impact of drops of water on PVC at a velocity of 400m/s results in the formation of numerous conchoidal brittle fractures. The small peaks on the brittle fracture surfaces indicate slight ductility. At high rates of deformation the amorphous thermoplastic exhibits less ductile behaviour. (21:1; 210:1; 2,100:1)

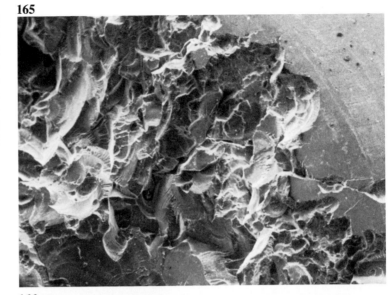

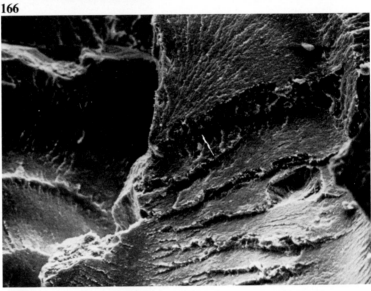

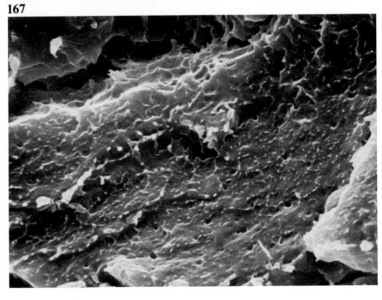

**168**

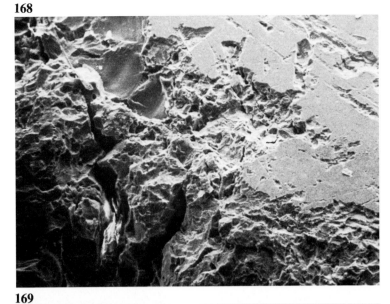

**168, 169.** The impact of drops of water at a velocity of 400m/s, droplet diameter 1.2mm, causes much conchoidal crumbling on a PMMA surface.

At high speeds of deformation this amorphous thermoplastic exhibits little ductile behaviour. (95:1; 470:1)

**169**

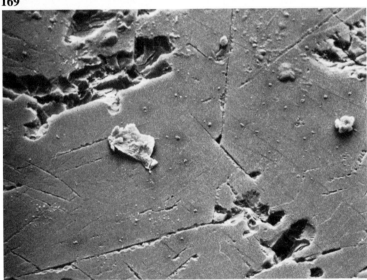

**170**

**170.** The impact of drops of water at a velocity of 400m/s, droplet diameter 1.2mm, causes many brittle fractures in PMMA. Many small splinters were lifted off. (1,800:1)

# EROSION

When a stream consisting of solid particles, liquid, gas or mixtures thereof, impinges upon a solid body in the form of a concentrated jet, it will usually cause channel-like erosions. The external form of the destructive effect depends on the flow conditions along the surface of the specimen. Wear is purely mechanical, no chemical reactions taking place.

The damage observed through a scanning electron microscope is similar to that produced by tangential bombardment with solid particles. The solid particles stretch the surface in the direction of flow and material is worn away, or abraded, as the lips and fibrils formed by the stretching are torn off.

**171, 172.** Inside surface of a PP pipe through which cooling water containing suspended sand had flowed. Wear was due to stretching of the surface and lips and fibrils being torn off. (2,200:1; 5,000:1)

**171**

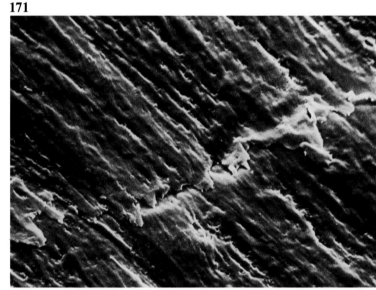

**172**

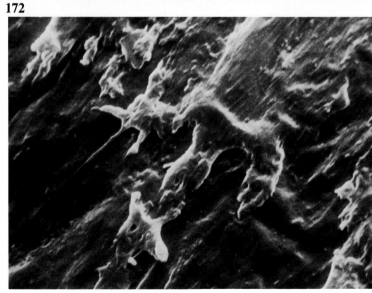

**173, 174.** Inside surface of a PE pipe through which water containing suspended sand had flowed. Wear was due to stretching of the surface zones and lips and fibrils being torn off. (550:1; 1,200:1)

**173**

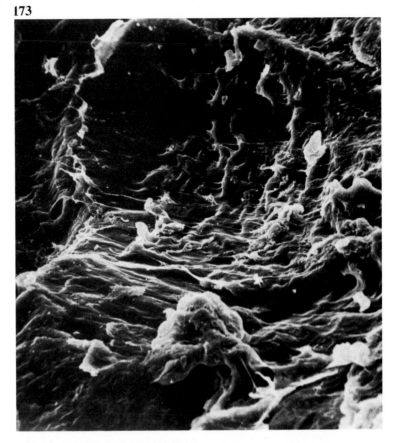

**174**

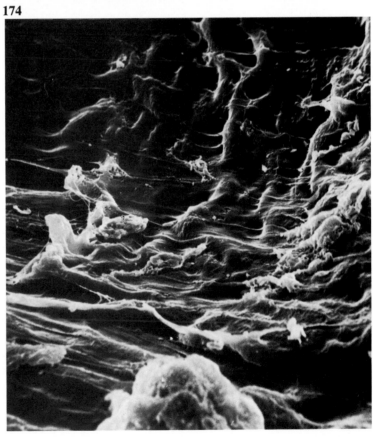

# CAVITATION

'Cavitation' results from the formation of cavities in a liquid, i.e. the formation of bubbles of vapour due to a local decrease in pressure. The implosion of these vapour bubbles (whose diameter is a few tenths of a millimetre) in the boundary layer between liquid and material surface causes damage which is referred to as cavitation. There is no material which will withstand cavitation indefinitely.

Cavitation due to flow and cavitation due to vibration can be distinguished. Flow cavitation occurs at points where there is increased rate of flow, where the pressure falls to below the vapour pressure. Known examples include ships' screws, hydro-turbines, elbows and nozzles. Vibration cavitation occurs when a vibrating wall is in contact with a liquid and is observed, for example, in the walls of ultrasonic baths.

A similarity between droplet impact and cavitation has been observed in various materials*. A high speed jet of liquid shoots out of imploded gas bubbles†. This has two types of effect on the adjoining surface:

1. The mechanical effect of the microjet, similar to that produced by particles propelled at high speed. Stress fracture symptoms are produced, e.g. lips, peaks, fibrils, and/or brittle fracture surfaces.

2. Vibrational stresses due to the quick succession of jet impacts.

*Engel, L. and Klingele, H. Rasterelektronenmikroskopische Untersuchungen von Metallschäden, Gerling Institut für Schadenforschung und Schadenverhütung GmbH, Cologne, 1974.

†Lauterborn, W., Hensch, K. and Bader, F. Hochfrequenzkinematografische und holografische Untersuchungen zur Dynamik von Kavitationsblasen, DFG-Forschungsbericht, Bonn, 1974.

**175**

**175.** Vibration cavitation produced in the laboratory on an HDPE specimen in water. The damaged surface is composed of a mass of small craters. In the peripheral zone, where there was less stress, only a few fibres became detached from the surface. (24:1)

**176.** The initial stages of damage can be recognised in this picture of the slightly stressed peripheral zone of a cavitation area. The many jets which hit the surface represent an alternating stress which leads to dynamic fatigue cracks. Since these are aligned parallel to the orientation due to the manufacturing process, the low strength at right angles to the direction of orientation becomes noticeable. Fibres near the surface are completely detached from the base material. (240:1)

**176**

**177.** Section from **176**. (1,200:1)

**177**

**178, 179.** Vibration cavitation produced in the laboratory on an HDPE specimen in water. As in the case of droplet impact, the impact of numerous jets results in a crater landscape. Deep holes are formed in between completely frayed areas. At the bottom of the crater one can see the start of destruction by alternating stresses, in the short fibre ends which are still located in a compact matrix. (120:1; 600:1)

**178**

**179**

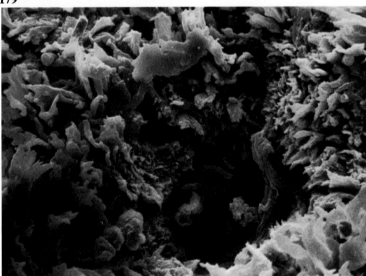

**180.** Vibration cavitation produced in the laboratory on an HDPE specimen in water. Fraying at the bottom of a crater. (2,400:1)

**180**

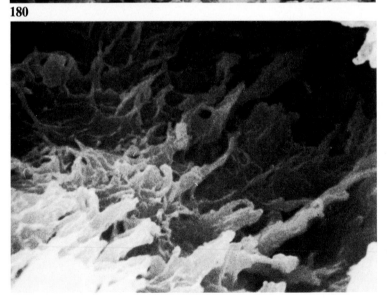

# Physico-chemical surface damage

## SURFACE DAMAGE CAUSED BY CHEMICALS

Polymers are attacked by many liquids and gases (page 250). There are cases where certain chemicals attack only certain constituents of a multi-component polymeric material. The butadiene contained in ABS, for example, is removed by chromic acid, whilst the SAN surrounding it remains untouched. This kind of selective solution leaves holes in the surface. The glass fibres contained in GRP materials are dissolved out by hydrofluoric acid which may diffuse into the material, or by sodium hypochlorite in caustic soda.

A commonly encountered physical effect is water absorption, which is specially apparent in polyamides where, on the other hand, it increases toughness. Swellings due to water leave shrinkage patterns behind after the specimen has dried out. Here it should be noted that specimens are subjected to a vacuum and thus dried and de-aerated, both when being prepared for the scanning electron microscope and during examination with that instrument.

**181.** Outer surface of a 5mm thick PVC sheet which had been immersed in acetone for 90 minutes. (5,000:1)

**181**

**182.** Relating to **181**: after the specimen has been dried, shrinkage patterns are observed on the surface. Examination of a cross-section of the specimen showed it to have numerous cracks running parallel to the surface (cf. **453**). (5,000:1)

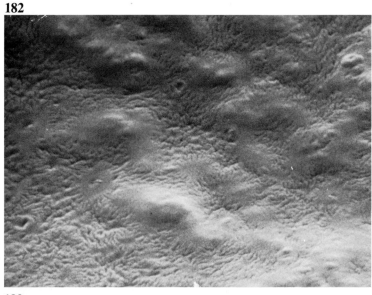

**183, 184.** Effect of a 20:80 acetone/water mixture on ABS (10 minutes' immersion at 20°C).

Internal stresses around the rubber particles, present initially, are released by the solvent so that bulge-like formations are produced. (1,000:1; 10,000:1)

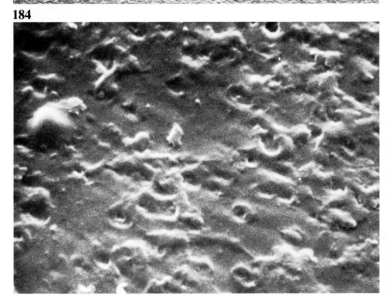

**185, 186.** Effect of 60% chromic acid on ABS (30 minutes). The butadiene rubber particles have been dissolved out. (1,000:1; 10,000:1)

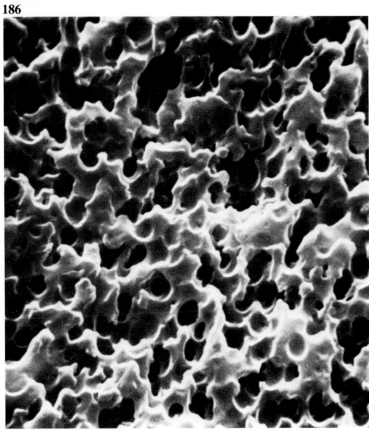

**187–189.** The effect of a 20:80 chloroform/alcohol mixture on ABS at 20°C can only be seen under 20,000 times magnification, which shows the development of a fine spherical structure. This is presumably a base structure resulting from the polymerisation process. The holes are due to butadiene rubber particles (cf. **186**). (2,000:1; 10,000:1; 20,000:1)

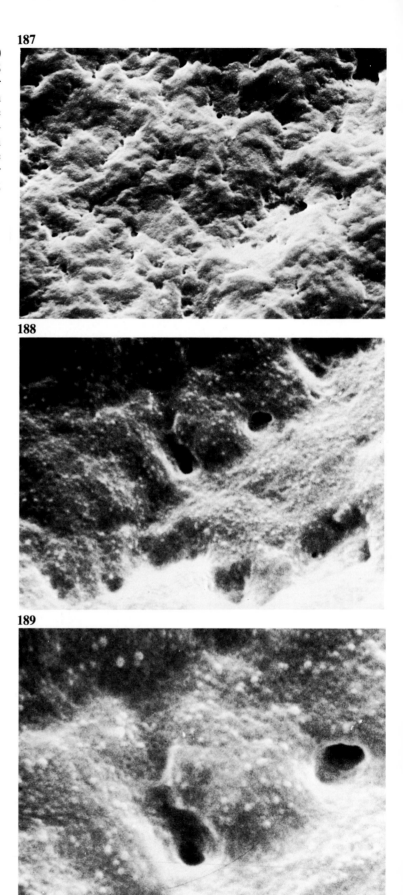

**190, 191.** Effect of a 20:80 acetone/water mixture on SAN for 20 minutes. The holes formed are presumably oriented according to the base structure due to the polymerisation process. (5,000:1; 10,000:1)

**190**

**191**

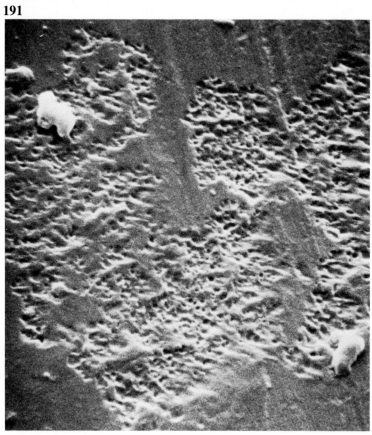

**192.** Close to a bonded PVC pipe joint, blisters were formed due to split adhesive. These were probably caused by the vapour pressure of the solvent which had diffused into the PVC. (24:1)

**192**

**193**

**193.** The blister (from **192**) was cut open and the structure of a radial tear fracture became visible underneath. The V-patterns in the crack structure prove the propagation from the centre to the edge of the blister. (22:1)

**194.** Tear fracture at the periphery of a raised blister (from **192**). The ductile crack structures point towards the softening effect of the solvent which has diffused into the material. (200:1)

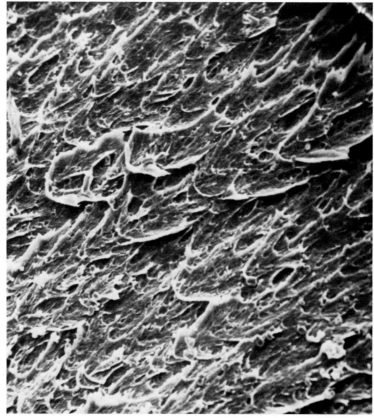

**195.** Tensile stress fracture at the centre of the blister (from **192**). (1,000:1)

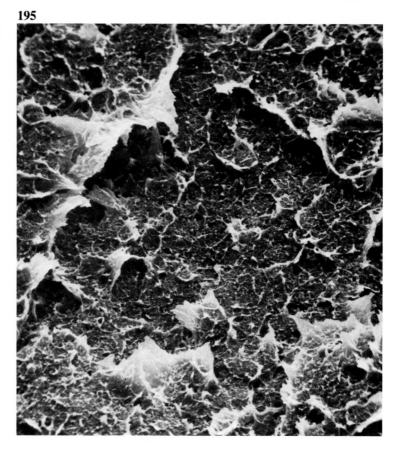

**196**

**196, 197.** The fracture surface of a glass fibre reinforced polyester specimen was immersed in hydrofluoric acid which completely dissolved the glass fibres without attacking the resin. (110:1; 1,000:1)

**197**

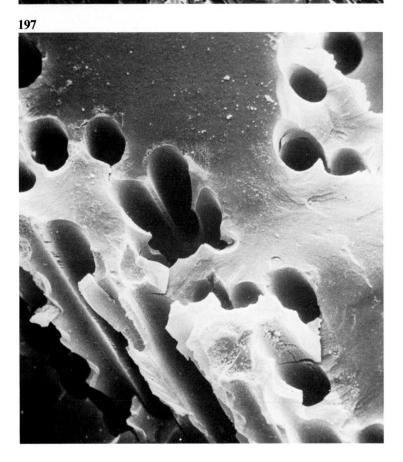

**198.** See caption to **199** and **200**. (140:1)

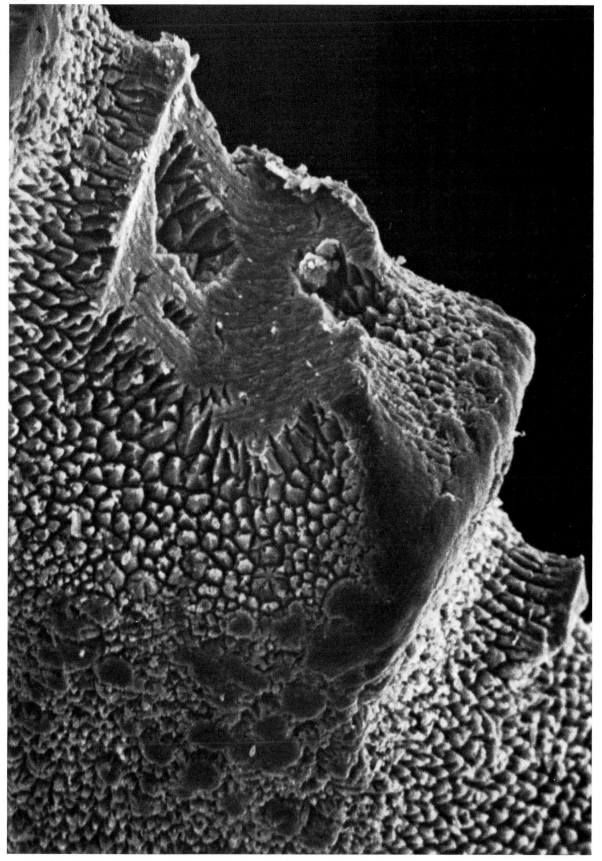

**199, 200.** A POM gear wheel, which had been in operation in the atmosphere of a boiler room, failed on account of considerable shrinkage. The oriented crystalline superstructures and the micro-porosity point towards strong post-crystallisation. The porosity is due to the difference in densities between the amorphous ($1.05 \text{g/cm}^3$) and the partially crystalline ($1.4 \text{g/cm}^3$) state. Breakdown along the crystalline superstructure started mainly at the mechanically stressed tooth flanks. Residues of mechanical contact in **198** and **199**. The damage was presumably caused by oil vapours. (575:1; 5,500:1)

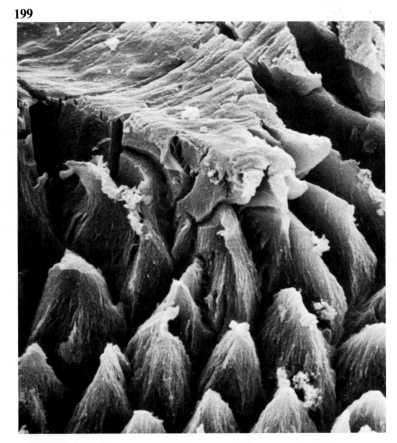

199

200

# UV IRRADIATION

The high energy ultra-violet rays cause changes which lead to brittleness and surface cracks. After intensive UV irradiation, a polymer can disintegrate into small pieces measuring a few micrometers.

Polymers can be protected against the effects of UV rays by incorporating suitable stabilisers. The effect of these stabilisers varies and not all polymers are equally easy to stabilise.

**201.** Stabilised pigments in an alkyd paint shielded the areas underneath from the effects of UV radiation. This formed little pedestals bearing pigment particles at the top. (10,000:1)

**201**

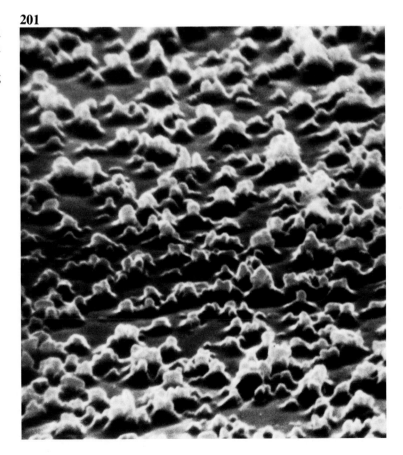

**202.** A POM specimen was irradiated with UV light in the laboratory for 1000 hours. Cracks appeared along the peripheral zone of the irradiated area. (200:1)

**202**

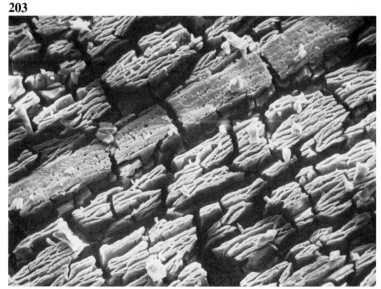

**203**

**203, 204.** Major disintegration can be seen near the centre of the irradiated area (from **202**). The direction of the cracks indicates orientation during processing, whilst the absence of stretched zones indicates embrittlement. (200:1; 2,000:1)

**204**

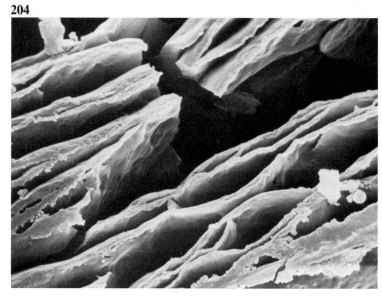

# WEATHERING

The results of weathering are due to the following factors:

UV rays

Solar heat

Absorption of water and substances in the atmosphere

Expansion effect of frozen water

Attack by bacteria and fungi

Attack by foreign bodies such as hailstones.

The type of damage caused varies accordingly and may consist of shrinkage cracks, brittle fractures, stress cracking and mechanical damage.

**205, 206.** A chair made of glass fibre reinforced PA 6 (50% w/w) was subjected to weathering for 5 years. The surface became mat and a network of brittle cracks was formed. (240:1; 5,700:1)

205

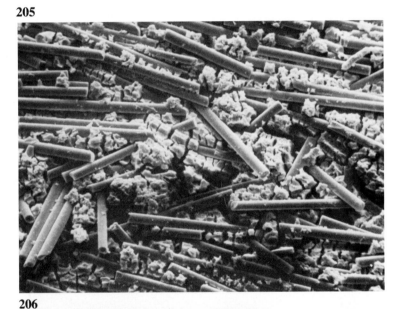

206

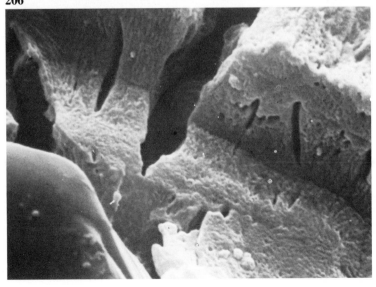

**208.** Original condition of PVC sheets before natural weathering. (2,000:1)

**208**

**209.** After 6 years' weathering the surface (from **208**) appears full of cracks and fissures. Neither stretched zones nor other mechanical influences are apparent. The damage was connected with wear. (2,000:1)

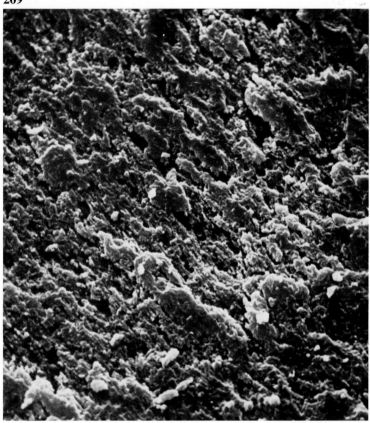

**209**

**207.** Another view of **205** and **206**. (5,700:1)

**210.** Original condition of PVC sheets before natural weathering. A section from **208**. (10,000:1)

**210**

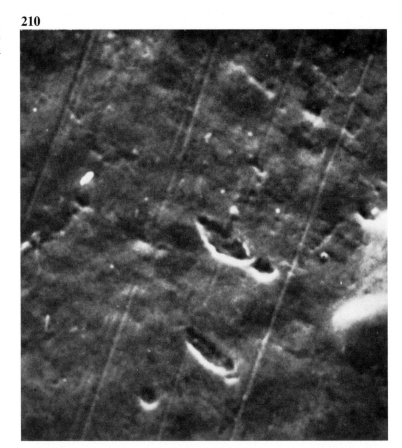

**211.** The PVC sheets after 6 years' weathering. A section from **209**. (10,000:1)

**211**

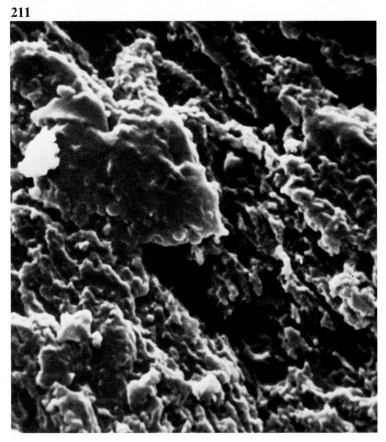

**212, 213.** Nine years' use and exposure to weathering caused a network of brittle cracks to form on the surface of a beer crate made from HDPE. The zones underneath had likewise become embrittled and splintered when the specimen for scanning electron microscope examination was cut out with a saw (bottom right in **212**). (24:1; 120:1)

**212**

**213**

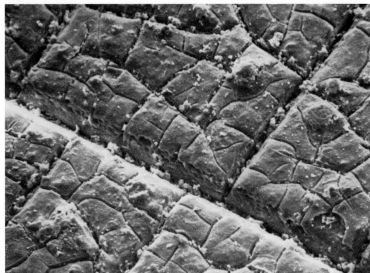

**214.** Brittle cracks on the surface of an HDPE beer crate which had been in use and exposed to weathering for 9 years. (600:1)

**214**

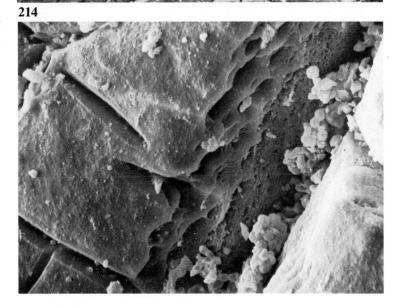

# EFFECT OF HIGH TEMPERATURE

The mechanical properties of polymeric materials greatly depend on the actual ambient temperature. As this increases, the strength and rigidity of the polymer decrease – in other words, the material softens. If the permissible maximum service temperature is greatly exceeded, thermoplastics and thermosets behave differently (see pages 12–14).

One must differentiate between heat distortion temperature and heat resistance. The heat distortion temperature characterises the mechanical and thermal performance of the material if subjected to force. The heat resistance on the other hand takes into account chemical changes due to exposure to high temperatures. Spontaneous thermal decomposition occurs at temperatures which lie far above the service temperature.

*Effect of high temperatures on thermoplastics*
As the temperature increases the material's strength decreases constantly, it starts to soften and, if the temperature is increased further, to flow. Ultimately it will decompose. One of the characteristic features of partially crystalline thermoplastics is the melting of the crystallites. This is why melt structures occur on heated surfaces. The characteristic features which indicate that a thermoplastic material has been exposed to heat are: soft and rounded melt structures, streaks, creases, pores, large peaks and columns.

One special feature is small, trough-like micro-craters formed around small inclusions. Surface zones which have been mechanically deformed tend to form lattice-type structures at elevated temperatures, which are aligned at right-angles to the direction of mechanical deformation.

*Effect of high temperatures on thermosets*
The mechanical properties of thermosets are very much less dependent on temperature than those of thermoplastics, because the chemically bound framework remains intact until thermal degradation sets in, so there is no flow.

Elastomers behave similarly, with the difference that the strength decreases more on account of the wide-mesh character of the framework (see **7**).

**215, 216.** Too high a temperature (310°C instead of the normal temperature of 250°C) was used to weld this PVC specimen by heated tool welding. This resulted in pronounced material flow, thermal degradation with formation of gas, and blistering.

In the fracture surface of the weld (top half of **215**) one can see streaks which show hardly any joins, or none at all, on either side. The smooth, unjoined areas clearly differ from the rougher fracture surfaces (**216**). The surface of the bead formed during welding (bottom half of **215**) likewise shows the typical melt structures and smooth, rounded surfaces. (21:1; 100:1)

**215**

**216**

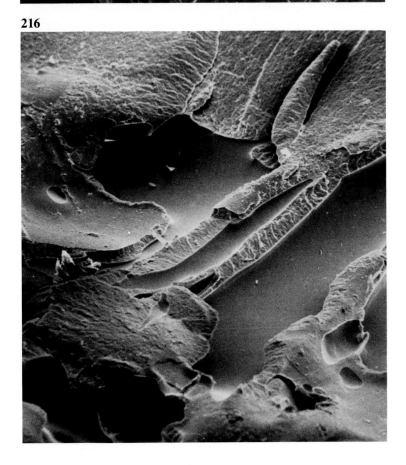

**217.** The welding fault from **216**. Smooth surfaces, blisters, rough surface (on left), fracture, bulging surface. (500:1)

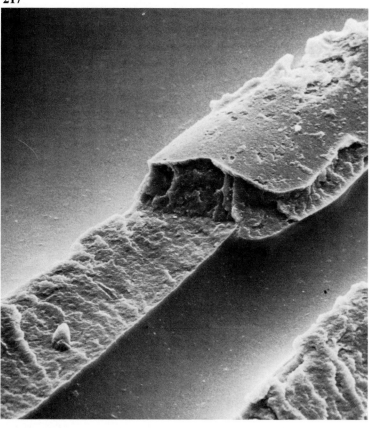

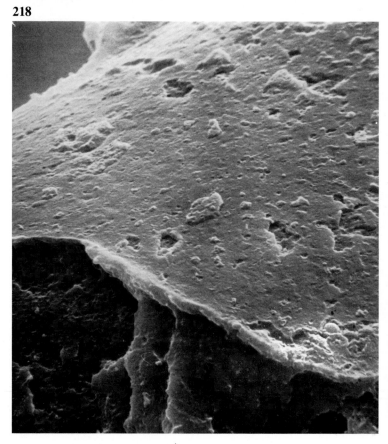

**218.** Welding fault (from **217**) with fracture and bulging surface. (2,000:1)

**219, 220.** Too high a temperature (470°C instead of the normal 310°C) was used when hot air welding this PVC specimen. Signs of material flow appeared on the surface of the melted material. Inside the material flow structures with cavities were formed, whose smooth finish makes them easy to distinguish from the rougher fracture surfaces (**220**). (100:1; 1,000:1)

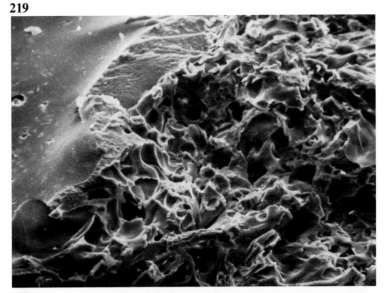

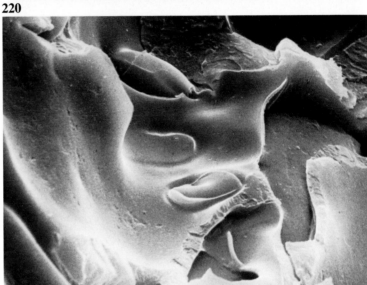

**221.** Too high a temperature (470°C instead of the normal 310°C) was used when hot air welding this PVC specimen. The resultant cavities and pores have a smooth and finely pitted surface (micro-craters). (10,500:1)

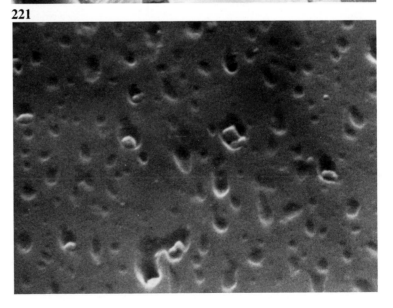

**222–224.** Too low a temperature (230°C instead of the normal 310°C) was used when hot air welding this PVC specimen. The surfaces to be joined have only been partly melted. The marks made by machining can still be clearly seen in the top right-hand corner of **222**. The characteristic features of softening are doughy structures with peaks, droplets and pores. (50:1; 200:1; 2,000:1)

**222**

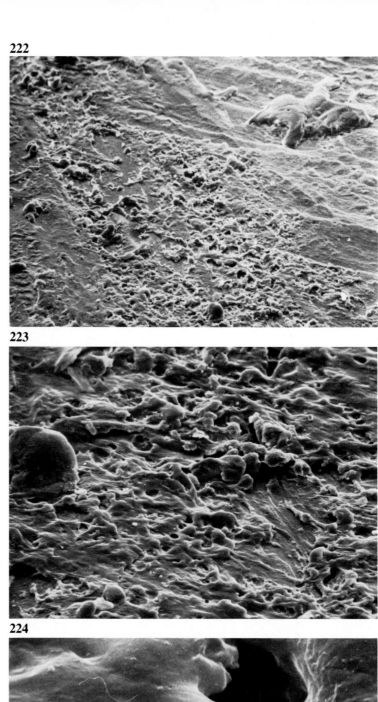

**223**

**224**

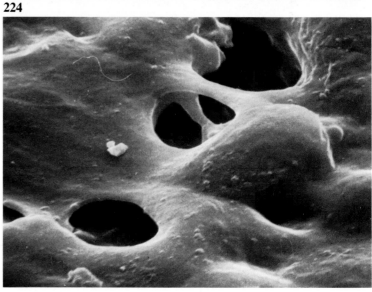

**225**

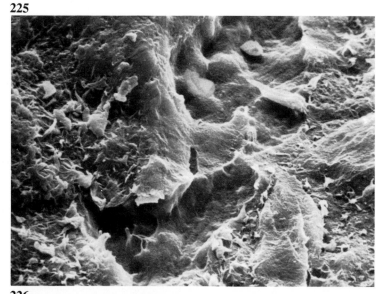

**225, 226.** Too high a temperature (360°C instead of the normal 280°C) was used when hot air welding this PE specimen. This produced cavities and pores. The surfaces of the former show skin-like creases (**226**).

Laboratory force fracture of welded zones (left-hand side in **225**) shows long drawn-out peaks and fibrils. (1,000:1; 5,000:1)

**226**

**227**

**227.** Too low a temperature (200°C instead of the normal 240°C) was used when hot air welding this PE specimen. Only one-third of the area to be joined had actually been welded, the rest being joined only at a few points (peak-like fracture structures, bottom left). (500:1)

**228, 229.** Too low a temperature (200°C instead of the normal 240°C) was used when hot air welding this PE specimen (from **227**). Only one-third of the area to be joined had actually been welded, the rest being melted only at several points. Under the influence of heat, the areas which had not been welded opened at right angles to the machining marks to form a lattice-type structure (**229**). (2,000:1; 10,000:1)

**228**

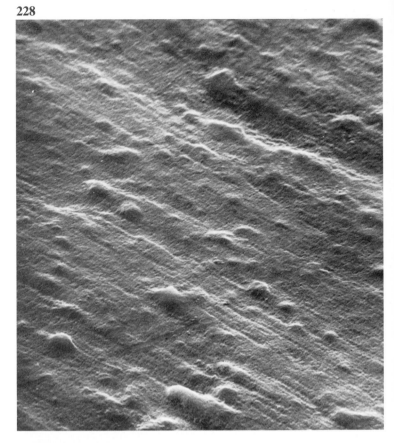

**229**

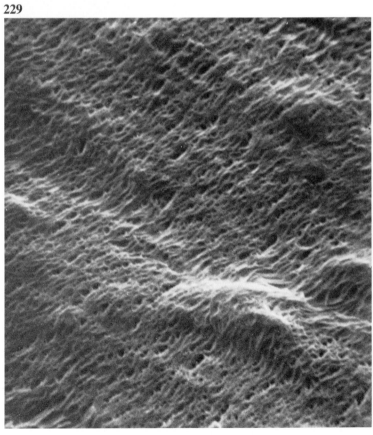

**230.** Too high a temperature (360°C instead of the normal 280°C) was used when hot air welding this PP specimen, resulting in the formation of a folded bead with a very smooth surface (right-hand half of photograph). (240:1)

230

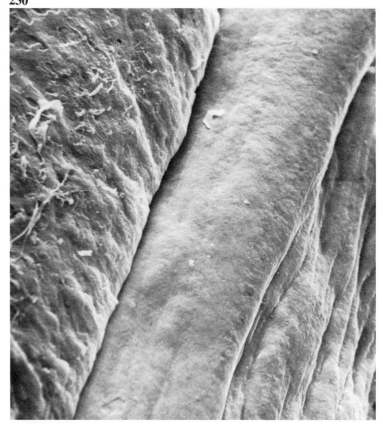

231

**231.** Smooth surface of weld bead (from **230**). (2,400:1)

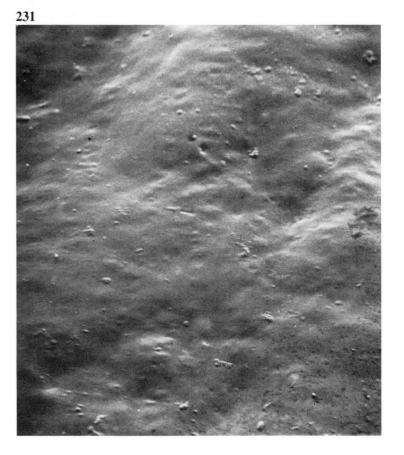

**232, 233.** Too high a temperature (360°C instead of the normal 280°C) was used when hot air welding this PP specimen. Adhesion faults are visible in the opened weld. These have a smooth surface. Also visible are numerous micro-craters around inclusions. (130:1; 1,300:1)

**232**

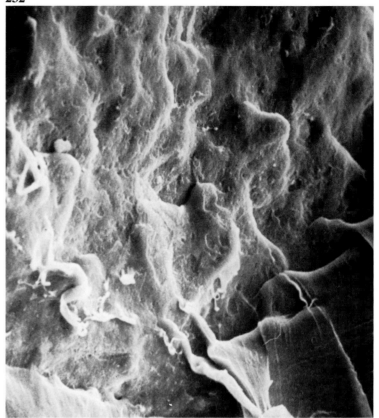

**233**

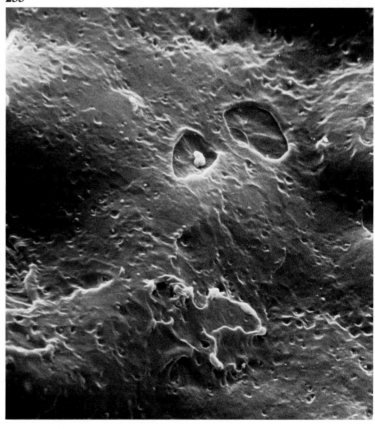

**234, 235.** Too high a temperature (360°C instead of the normal 280°C) was used when hot air welding this PP specimen. Cavities with a smooth surface can be seen in the opened weld (left-hand side of photograph). The extremely long fibrils, which extend from one wall of the cavity to the other, prove that these cavities have been widened at high temperatures. (240:1; 2,600:1)

**234**

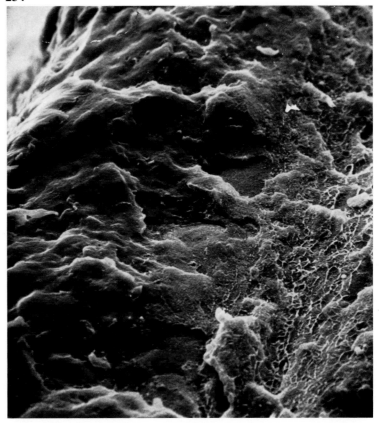

**235**

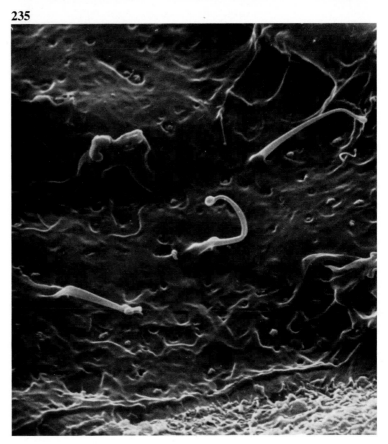

**236, 237.** Laser inclusions in SAN produced foam structures. The gas pressure wave is made apparent by the radial eruptions and viscous deformation of the surrounding material (bead formation). Focusing the beam onto deeper layers promotes bead formation. (105:1; 105:1)

**236**

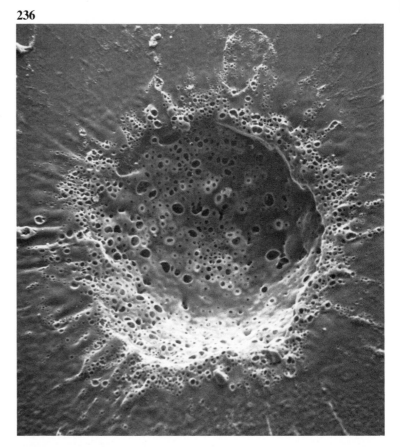

**237**

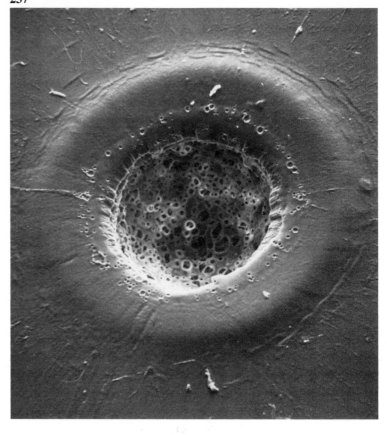

# BIOLOGICAL EFFECTS

Since polymers are organic in character, they can be attacked by the secretions of micro-organisms, especially those of bacteria and fungi. The process is similar to the rotting of wood when attacked by mould. Here, fungus hyphae start to grow on the cell walls, which they partly dissolve so that the wood disintegrates in the immediate vicinity (our own observations through the scanning electron microscope).

Rotting tests in compost have shown that PVC surfaces which had once been smooth are attacked by micro-organisms which form holes and scars. Soil acids, too, can attack polymeric materials.

**238, 239.** PVC surface which had been kept in compost, showing pits and scars made by micro-organisms. It is likely that the holes were caused by the root-like fungus hyphae shown in **239** (cf. **24** and **25**). (1,000:1; 10,000:1)

**238**

**239**

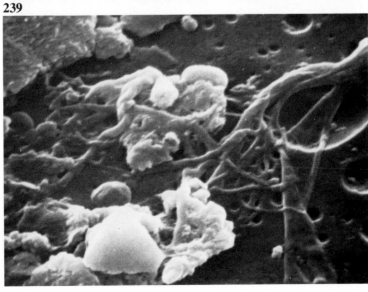

# 3. Fractures

Fracture is the unwanted separation of a formerly whole body into two or more pieces. Fracture may be caused through the wrong choice of material, faults in the material or operating conditions. The fracture surfaces of polymeric materials show many characteristic features which enable the destructive influences to be recognised.

# Mechanical fractures

## LOAD FRACTURES

Thermoplastics, thermosets and elastomers vary in their deformation characteristics. In thermoplastics, the tangled-up thread-like macromolecules are stretched and oriented by increasing loads and tend to separate from one another (**240**).

**240**

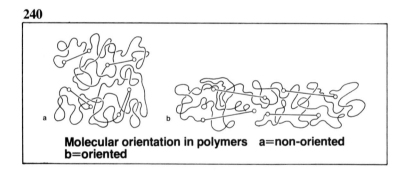

**Molecular orientation in polymers   a=non-oriented
b=oriented**

This stretching process requires time so that the occurrence of deformation to the point where fracture occurs is governed by the rate of loading. In addition, this kind of re-arrangement is made easier by elevated temperatures. The molecules are more capable of adapting to applied stresses at slow deformation rates and elevated temperatures than if the stress is applied quickly and suddenly and at low temperatures.

Thermosets, on the other hand, are difficult to deform because of the high degree of cross-linkage of their macromolecules. Elastic deformation is therefore greater than in thermoplastics, and plastic and visco-elastic deformation less. Hence the tendency for thermosets to form brittle fractures.

The partially entangled macromolecules of elastomers exhibit mainly elastic deformation (**242**) because of their low cross-linking density and the slight effect of the secondary bonding (entropy-elastic or rubbery state). Fracture occurs after a large amount of elastic elongation (above the glass transition temperature) due to breaking of the molecule chains. The residual deformation is relatively slight and may be recognised by the short peaks and fibrils.

## Normal stress fracture

When external stresses are applied to materials they stretch like fibres. When the two parts separate, the ends rebound, form peaks, and thicken (**1e** and **241**). Separation occurs at right-angles to the tensile axis.

**241**

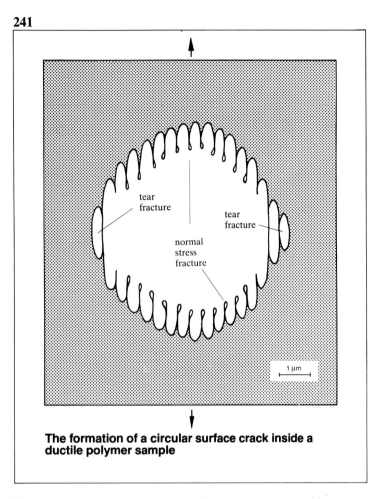

tear fracture

tear fracture

normal stress fracture

1 µm

**The formation of a circular surface crack inside a ductile polymer sample**

**242.** Elliptical cavities open up around inclusions in rubber when a tensile stress is applied. After fracture has occurred, peaks and fibrils are formed in the constriction areas. (200:1)*

**242**

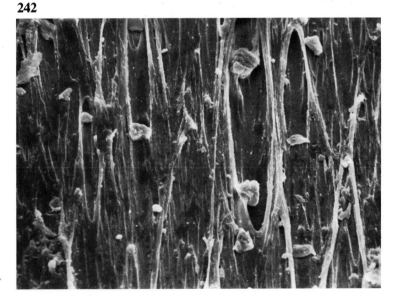

*Kern, W. F. Anwendungsbeispiele der Rastermikroskopie, Kautschuk + Gummikunststoffe, 1977, Heft 4, S. 237.

## Tear fracture

Normal stresses, unevenly distributed over a cross-sectional area, e.g. bending stresses, can cause the material to tear from an external or an internal surface, e.g. starting from a fault in the material. The peaks will then be at an angle to the fracture surfaces (**241**). If the elongation is uniformly distributed, walls are pulled up along the crack front which remain visible in both fracture surfaces after their separation, as beads with wavy crests (**244**). Other characteristic features of tear fractures are V or U-shaped patterns whose tips point in the opposite direction to the direction in which the fracture is spreading (**243**).

**243**

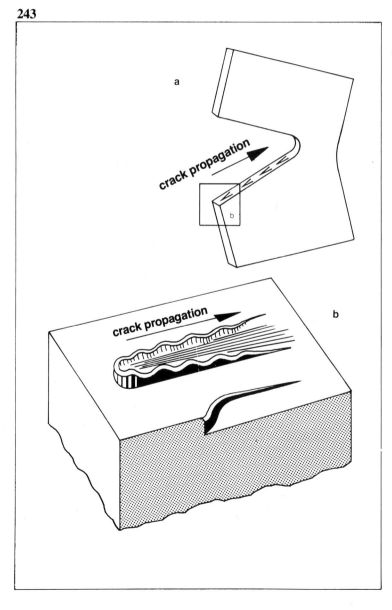

**243.** U- or V-shaped ramps, whose tips point in the direction opposite to crack propagation, are the characteristic feature of tear fracture in polymeric materials. Walls which have been pulled up form wavy beads after separation.

**244**

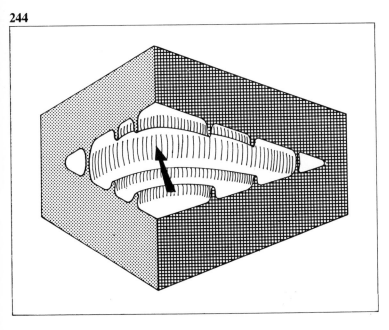

**244.** Tear fracture on the exposed surface of a specimen with large cross-sectional area. Because of the uniform stretching near the surface, not many peaks (columns) are pulled up, but only a complete wall. After this has separated, stretching or separation of a second wall occurs, and so on. The collapsed walls show a fibril structure which indicates the direction of stretching.

## Shear fracture

The failure of polymeric materials can be initiated by exceeding the critical shear stress.

Stretching of polymeric materials at the areas of separation ultimately results in the formation of lips and peaks on the two related fracture surfaces which point towards each other (**245**). Only where there are two related fracture surfaces is it possible to distinguish fracture due to shear failure from tear fracture. The separation mechanism is that of a normal stress fracture or of a tear fracture since no sliding along definable planes can occur as in metals.

**245**

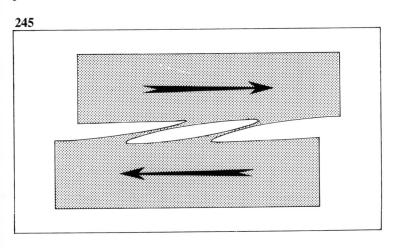

**245.** Shear failure in a polymer.

**Crazes.** Crazes are normal, small cracks due to stress, which cover a limited area. They relieve loaded parts of the material. They are, therefore, stabilised stress cracks whose separation surfaces are bridged by stretched fibrils and films (**246** and **247**). Fibril diameter 0.01–0.1$\mu$m.

Crazes can be formed on exposed surfaces as well as inside a component and thus have semi-circular or circular boundaries. In a transparent polymer it is possible to see the extent of the circle with the naked eye (stress whitening). Seen through the scanning electron microscope, opened-up crazes show the following characteristics: curved boundaries which are in clear contrast to the residual force fracture, and signs of ductile force fracture, i.e. peaks and fibrils.

Accordingly, crazes represent the initial stage of a ductile force fracture. Crazes are formed in homogeneous materials under continuous, slow tensile stress and not as a result of impact stress. They may therefore be compared in their effect with creep failure encountered in metals. In rubber modified polymers, crazes are also produced through impact.

In opened crazes one normally distinguishes between a central, normal stress zone and an adjacent tear zone (**241**). The concentric expansion of crazes can be observed by the V-shaped marks which are produced.

**246**

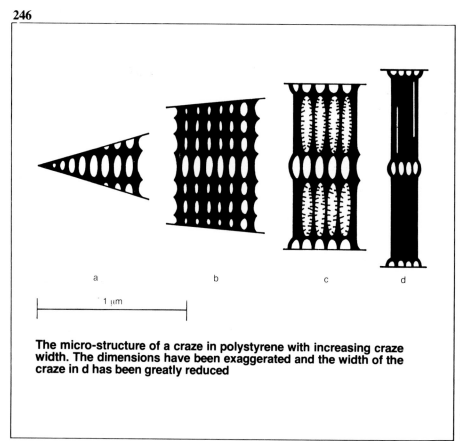

a     b     c     d

1 μm

**The micro-structure of a craze in polystyrene with increasing craze width. The dimensions have been exaggerated and the width of the craze in d has been greatly reduced**

Hull, D. The microstructure and properties of crazes, from: Deformation and Fracture of High Polymers, Plenum Press, New York, 1973.

**247.** Micro-structure at the tip of a craze.*

*Hull, D. The microstructure and properties of crazes, from: Deformation and Fracture of High Polymers, Plenum Press, New York, 1973.

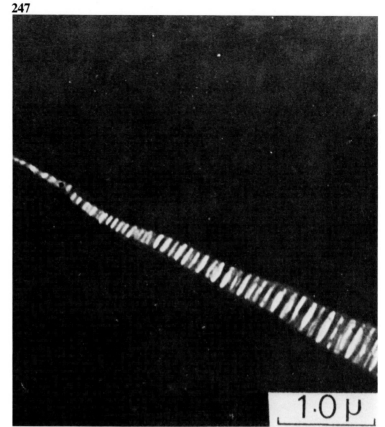

**248.** Surface crazes in PS, formed at room temperature and clearly differentiated from the split residual force fracture. The main crack spread from left to right at the top. Two smaller crazes came from the opposite side of the sample. (22:1)

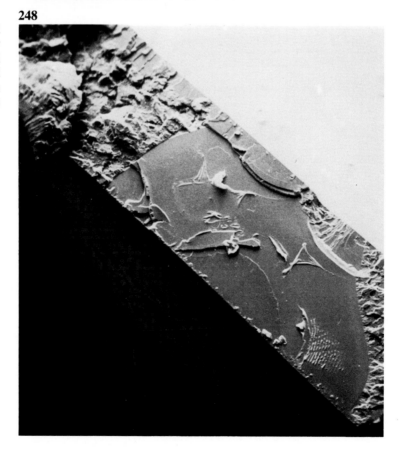

**249, 250.** Opened-up craze in PS (from **248**). In a largely level fracture surface separate ductile deformed films and fibrils were formed. Altogether, this is a low-deformation fracture with the characteristic features of load fracture. (550:1; 2,200:1)

**249**

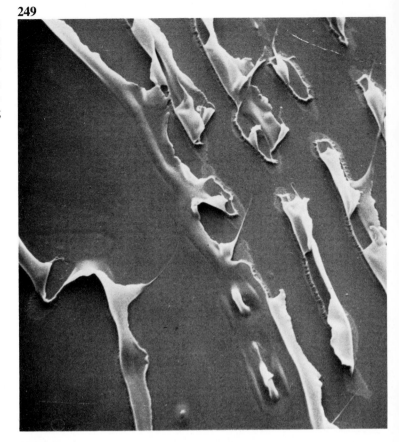

**250**

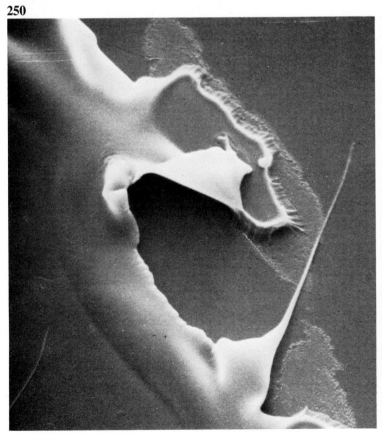

**251.** Two crazes formed at room temperature in SAN (left and front of picture). The fissured load fracture runs from the right to the back. (24:1)

**251**

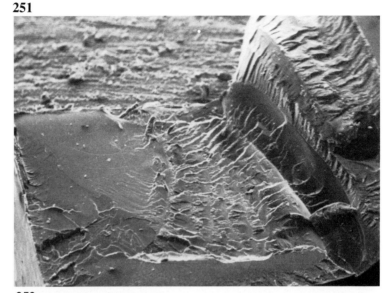

**252**

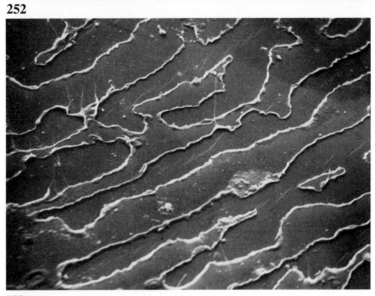

**252, 253.** Opened-up craze in SAN (from **251**). In a largely level fracture surface separate ductile deformed films and fibrils were formed. Altogether, this is a low-deformation fracture with the characteristic features of load fracture. (650:1; 6,500:1)

**253**

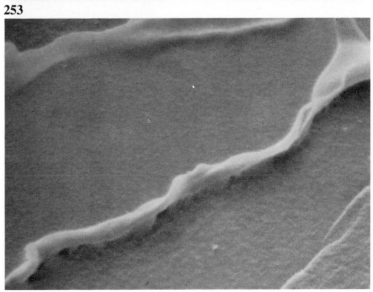

**254, 255.** At room temperature, several crazes formed simultaneously on the surface of an ABS tensile specimen.

In **254** two rough surface crazes, whose levels are staggered with respect to each other, can be clearly distinguished. At the top of the photographs there are also tensile cracks. (23:1; 110:1)

**254**

**255**

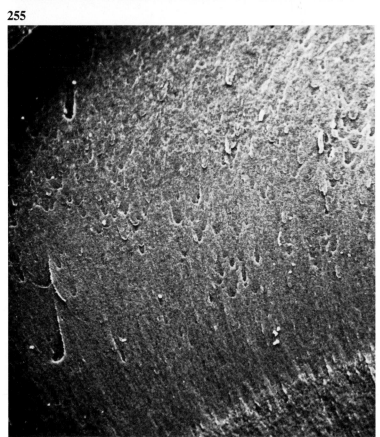

**256.** Normal stress zone of an opened-up craze (from **254**) near the surface of an ABS tensile specimen, with peak structure of ductile fracture. (11,500:1)

256

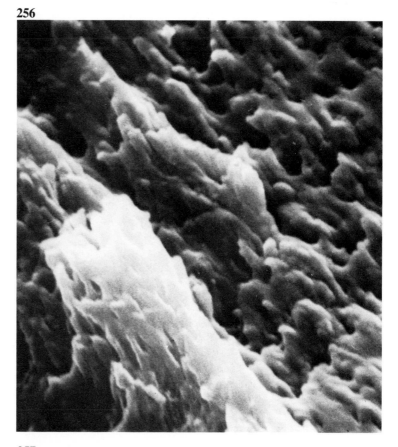

257

**257.** Crack zone of a craze in ABS (from **254**). (11,000:1)

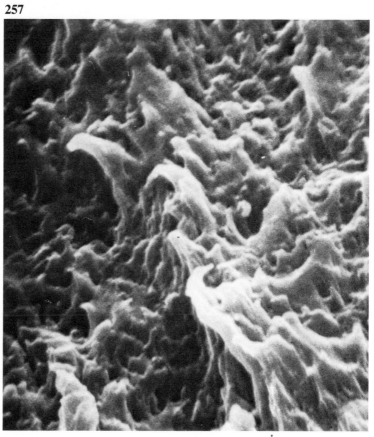

**258, 259.** Craze formed at room temperature inside an ABS test specimen. The circular craze is divided into a likewise circular normal stress crack at the centre, and a radially propagating tear crack (**247**). (24:1; 120:1)

**258**

**259**

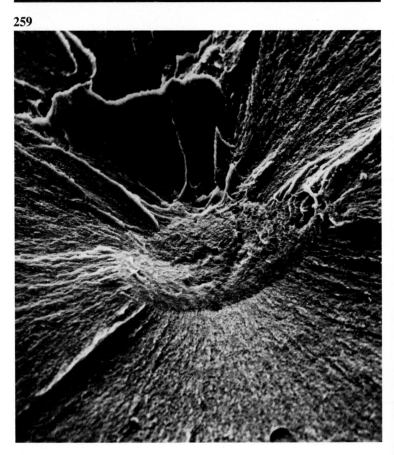

**260**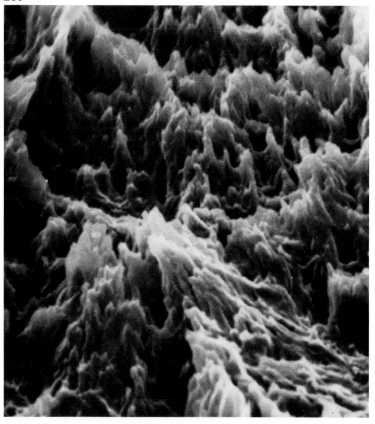

**260.** Ductile normal stress fracture (from **258**) with peak structure at the centre of a craze in ABS (cf. **247**). (12,000:1)

**261**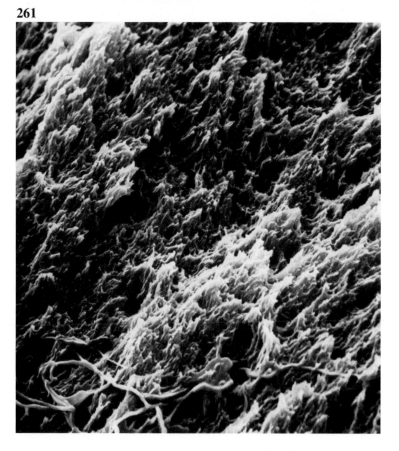

**261.** In the circular zone of an internal craze (from **258**), the obliquely slanted peaks indicate tear failure. Torn-off craze fibrils can be seen at bottom left in the photograph. (2,400:1)

**262.** The opened-up craze near the edge of this PVC tensile test specimen is composed of a normal stress crack (right at the front of **262**) and a tear zone (light coloured area with steps in **263**). At the back one can see the rough force fracture. (22:1)

**262**

**263.** Final part of the tear zone of a craze in PVC (from **262**). The top of the photograph shows residual stress fracture. (105:1)

**263**

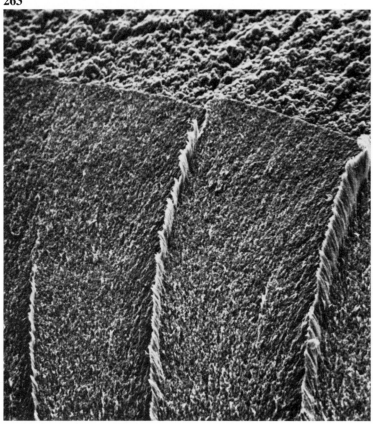

**264, 265.** Obliquely slanted fibrils, diameter about 0.1μm, at the end of a craze in PVC indicate tear failure. Residual force fracture follows at the top right of **264**. (2,000:1; 5,000:1)

264

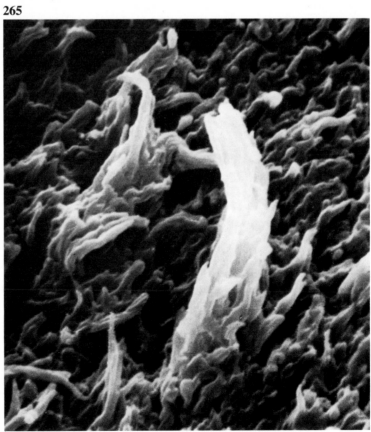

265

**266.** A PE pipe subjected to 80°C and internal pressure, fractured after 300 hours. A craze propagated concentrically around a calcium stearate agglomerate measuring 5µm in diameter. After the craze had penetrated two-thirds of the cross-sectional area, the remaining third failed spontaneously. (26:1)

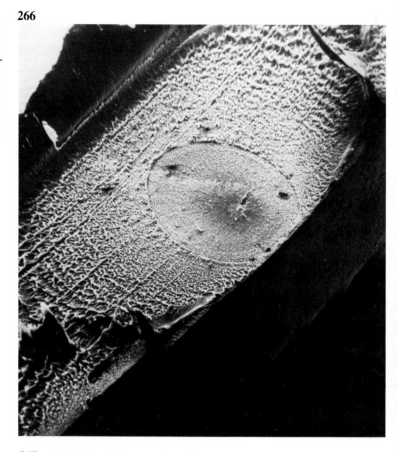

**267.** Normal stress zone at the centre of the craze. (1,300:1)

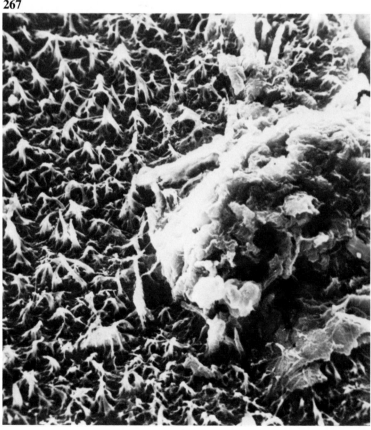

**268**

**268, 269.** A PS sample was tested under conditions of repeated tensile stress. This produced a craze inside the sample, which then propagated concentrically as a tear crack. The V-shaped marks in **269** show the radial spread of the crack (cf. **242**). When the crack had passed through half the cross-sectional area, load fracture occurred, whose micro-structure differs from that of a craze. (23:1; 220:1)

**269**

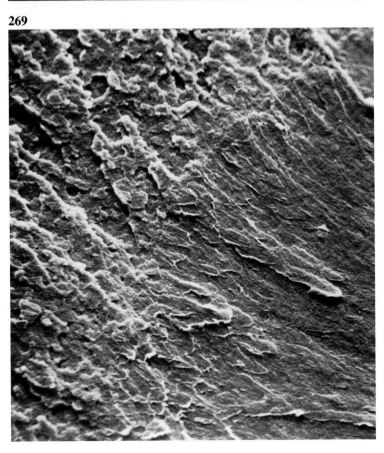

**Ductile tension-overload fractures.** According to our observations through the scanning electron microscope we have arbitrarily divided ductile fractures into two groups, the criterion being the lengths of the fibrils remaining in the fracture.

Polymers with high plastic deformation up to fracture – length of remaining fibrils $> 10\mu$m.

Polymers with low plastic deformation up to fracture – length of remaining fibrils $1–10\mu$m.

According to this classification, fractures producing fibrils less than $1\mu$m long are said to be brittle (see pages 177–197).

*Polymers with high plastic deformation at break*
Polymers which will normally withstand a high degree of plastic deformation include PE, PP, PA, POM, PBTP, PETP, PTFE, PC, PVC and ABS.

**270.** Tear fracture at room temperature in a 0.3mm thick film made of plasticised PVC. Branching causes V- or U-shaped ramps parallel to the crack propagation direction. The tips of the ramps point in the direction opposite to that of crack propagation. (5,500:1)

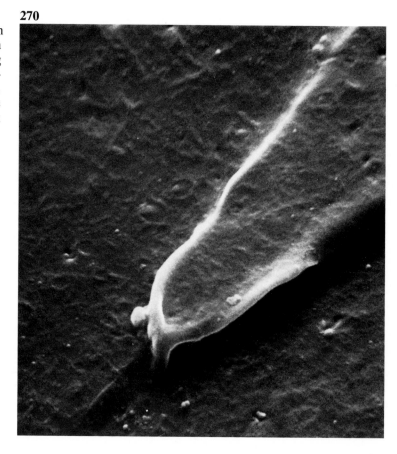
270

**271, 272.** Ductile tear failure produced at room temperature (**271**) and normal tensile failure (**272**) in injection moulded PU elastomer. The tensile crack spread from the bottom to the top and left behind wavy walls as it progressed. (250:1; 600:1)

**271**

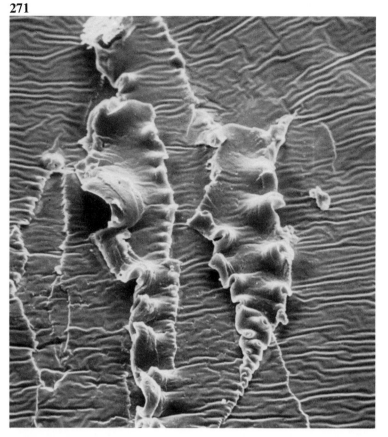

**272**

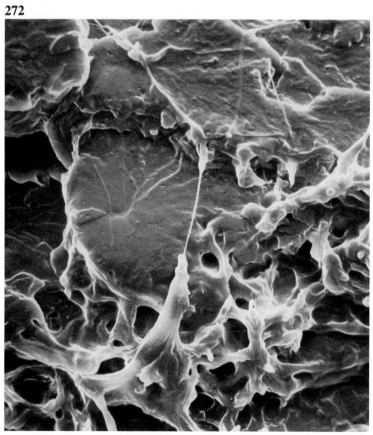

**273.** Tear failure in plasticised PVC at room temperature. The crack propagated along an approx. 0.3mm thick film from the top left-hand corner to bottom right. A few peaks and parallel fibril structures in pulled-up, wavy crests enable one to recognise the stretching that took place prior to fracture. Peak length about 20$\mu$m. Next to this, there are extremely smooth areas without visible deformation structures (cf. **272**). (550:1)

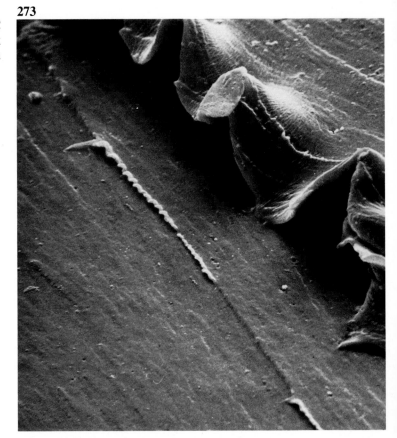

**274.** In the residual load fracture of a 0.3mm thick, plasticised PVC film, the crack propagated from the surface across the cross-sectional area (from bottom left to top right). The crack front is shown in the photograph as composed of three sections. The fibril structure is due to the folds which have been pulled up rather like a tablecloth. (2,400:1)

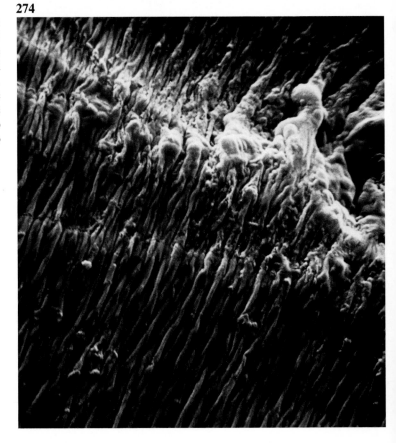

**275, 276.** A laboratory sample of LDPE subjected to a load of 7.85N/mm² fractured after 15 minutes at room temperature. The short loading period compared with **277** and **278** did not permit extremely long deformation bundles. In the fracture photograph peaks, rounded by rebounding and with diameters of around 20μm, predominate. (110:1; 550:1)

**275**

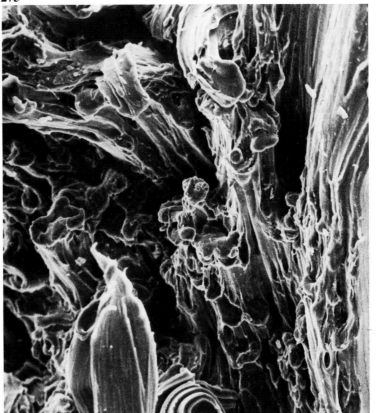

**276**

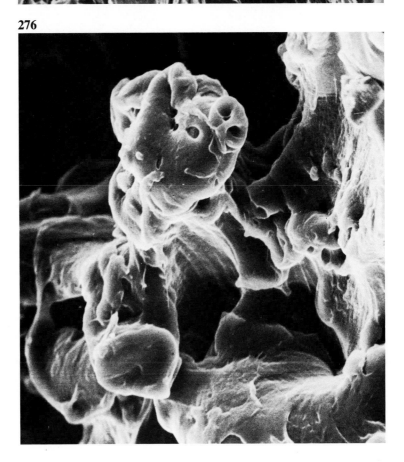

**277, 278.** A laboratory sample of LDPE was subjected to a load of 6.4N/mm² for 1,010 hours at room temperature. This long-term stress caused extreme flow of the material and therefore a marked constriction. In the micro-zone, too, marked constrictions of the long drawn-out bundles of material can be recognised. This led to the formation of oval voids similar to those which occur in ductile metals. (105:1; 525:1)

**277**

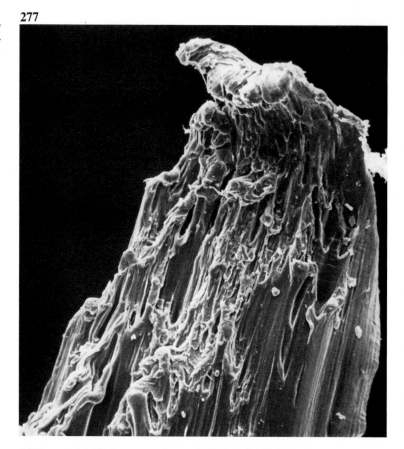

**278**

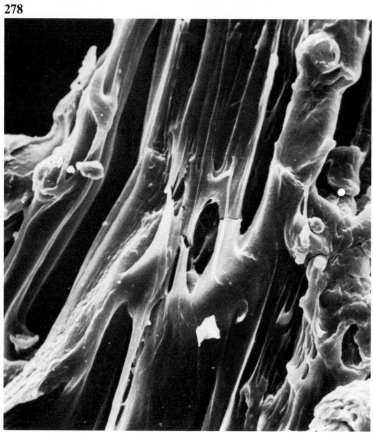

**279, 280.** A laboratory sample of HDPE was loaded with 8.8N/mm² and failed after 547 hours. There was little external constriction, the deforr.ation being absorbed by the micro-structure. Hardly any signs of peak formation can be seen near the surface where the crack begins. The arrangement of the fibrils in the crack surface, at right angles to the external surface, indicates that shear failure has occurred. Minimum fibril diameter 100nm. (25:1; 2,400:1)

**279**

**280**

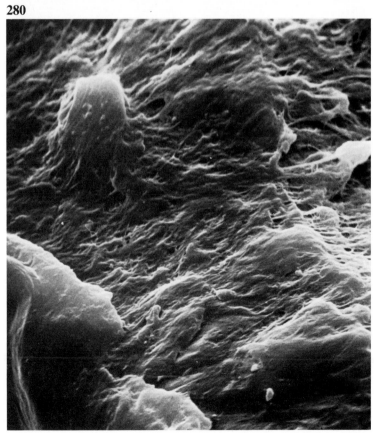

**281, 282.** The centre of the cross-sectional area (from **279**): tear fracture in HDPE with pronounced peak formation. Minimum fibril diameter $0.05\mu$m, maximum fibril length approx. $30\mu$m. (600:1; 2,400:1)

**281**

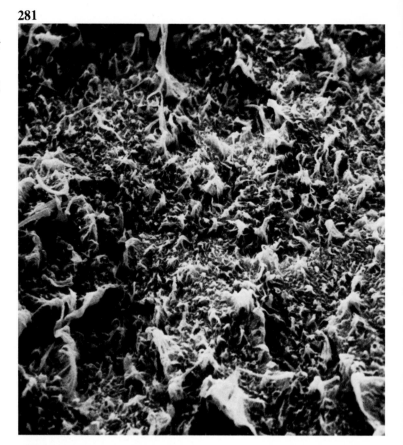

**282**

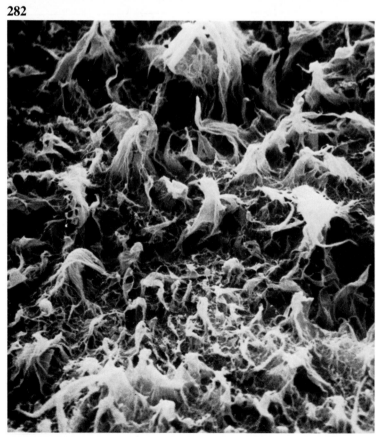

**283, 284.** Laboratory fracture in PP at room temperature, with marked external constriction.

The smallest visible fibrils have a diameter of $0.05\mu$m and are up to $75\mu$m long. (20:1; 1,000:1)

**283**

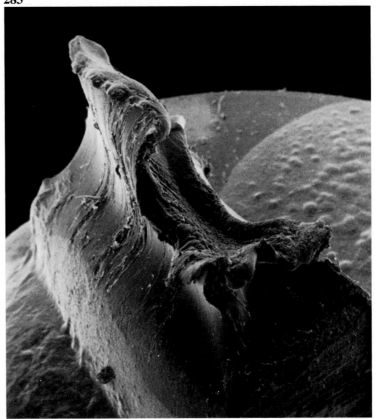

**284**

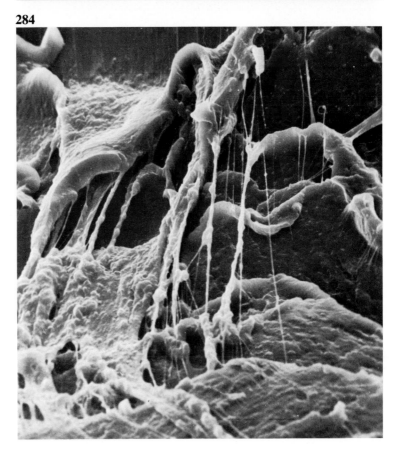

**285, 286.** Ductile residual fracture at the base of a tooth of a gear wheel made of PBTP. Peaks up to 10µm long prove ductile failure to have taken place. The smallest visible fibril diameters are around 0.05µm. (5,500:1; 5,500:1)

**285**

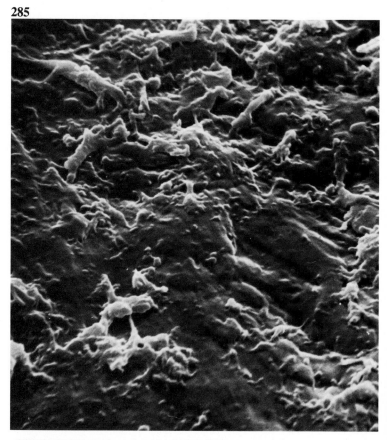

**286**

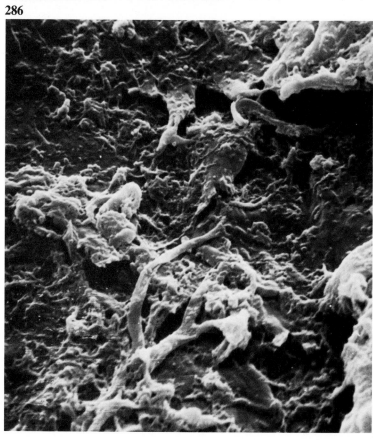

**287, 288.** A laboratory sample of POM was stressed at room temperature until failure occurred. The characteristic features of ductile failure can be distinguished: isolated peaks and fibrils about 10μm long.

The micro-porosity of the material is due to the manufacturing process and is caused by the transition from low to high density during crystallisation. (24:1; 2,400:1)

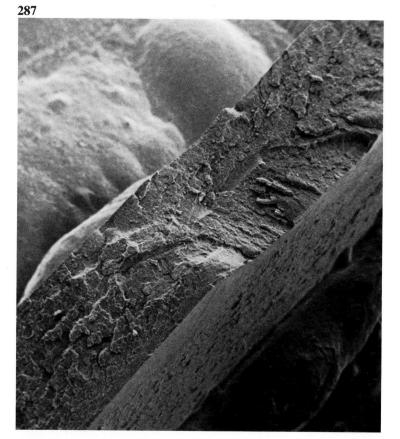

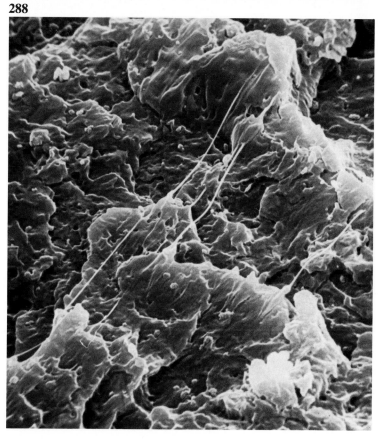

**289**

**289–291.** Fracture in PA at room temperature. A tear fracture first of all spread from a sprue. Its structure is characterised by V-patterns (**289**), oriented peaks and bands at right angles to the direction of crack propagation (**290**). In the residual fracture (**291**), long drawn-out fibrils and peaks can be distinguished as characteristic features of extreme ductile failure. (20:1; 2,700:1; 1,800:1)

**290**

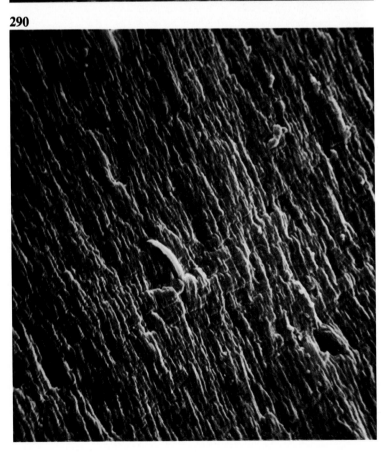

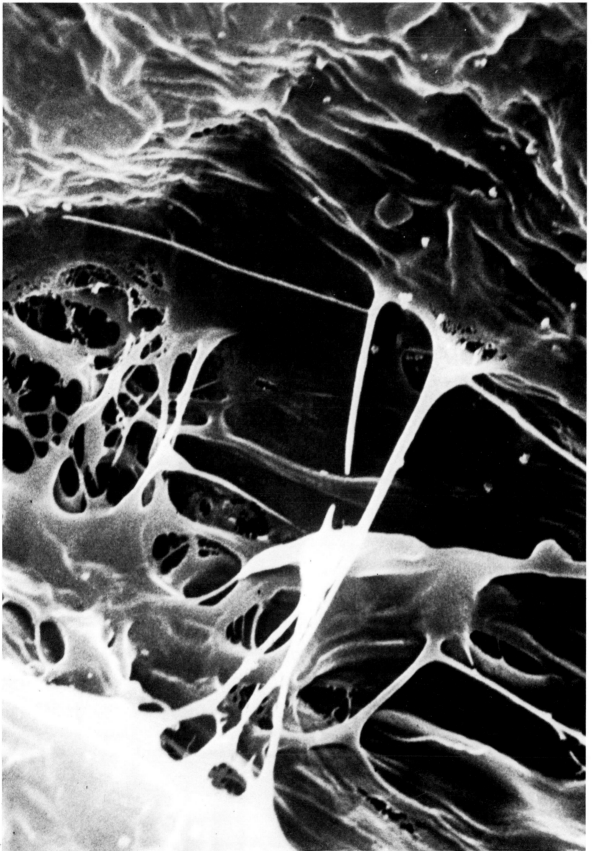

**292, 293.** A nylon 6 laboratory sample was briefly stressed at room temperature until failure occurred. Peaks and fibrils are produced and are characteristic features of ductile failure. The minimum fibril diameter is $0.1\mu$m, the longest fibril measures about $20\mu$m (**292**). (2,400:1; 1,200:1)

**292**

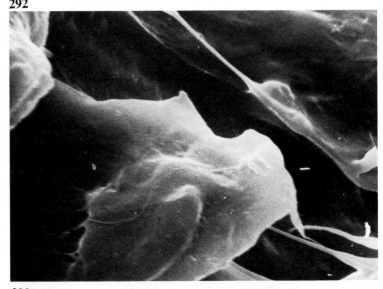

**293**

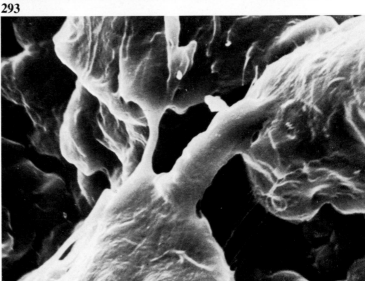

**294.** The spiral structure was formed through a fibril rebounding. (12,000:1)

**294**

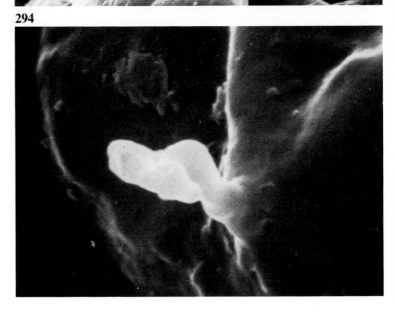

**295.** Ductile fracture of a viscose fibre at room temperature. Despite a high degree of stretching of the fibre as supplied, the fracture clearly shows the characteristic features of ductile failure, namely constriction and the formation of peaks. (2,000:1)

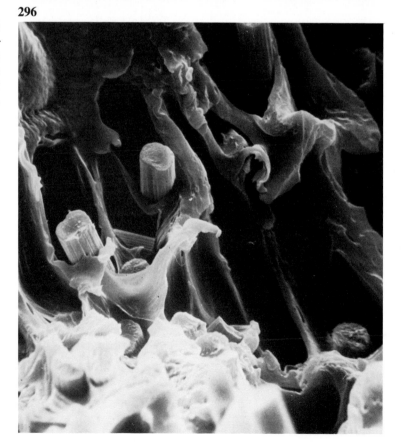

**296.** Fracture of nylon 6 with 17% carbon fibres, at room temperature. The appearance of the fracture surface is determined by the extreme ductility of the matrix and poor adhesion of the carbon fibres. (1,200:1)

**297, 298.** Fracture, at room temperature, of high impact glass fibre reinforced nylon 6 (30% w/w glass). Ductile failure occurred in the matrix. Because of the good adhesion of the polyamide, the free fibre ends are still covered with the polymer. (1,200:1; 6,000:1)

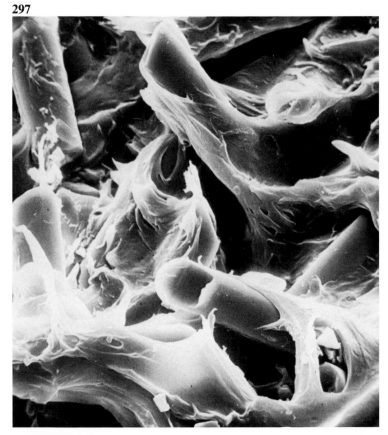

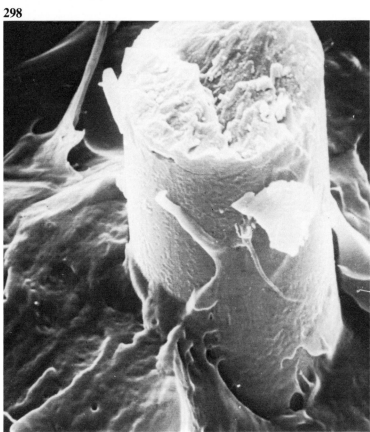

**299.** Fracture, at room temperature, of nylon 6 with 30% w/w chalk. The ductile fracture has been split up by the chalk particles. (1,100:1)

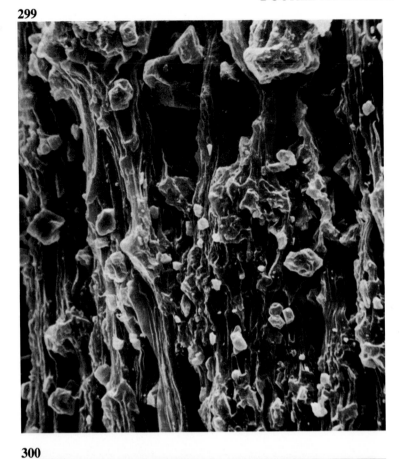

**300.** Ductile fracture in glass fibre reinforced PTFE at room temperature. A notable feature is the extreme stretching of the material and its excellent adhesion to the glass fibres. (2,400:1)

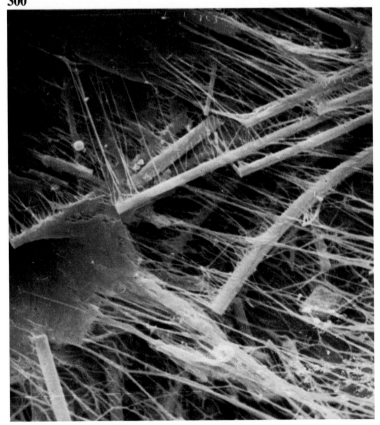

**301, 302.** Fracture in polypropylene reinforced with 30% w/w glass fibre. The characteristic features of ductile force fracture are:

– structures which have been pulled to pieces, with peaks and fibrils (fibril diameter about $0.1\mu$m; fibril length up to $80\mu$m).

– glass fibres, which have fractured at an angle and protrude from the fracture surface, or have left behind deep holes. Cf. vibration fracture, **384** and **385**. (1,100:1; 1,100:1)

**301**

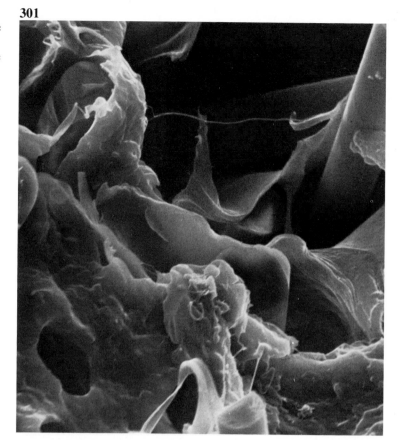

**302**

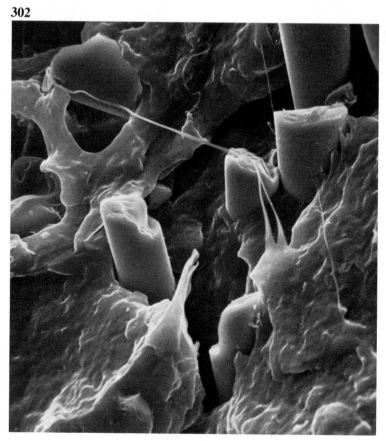

**303, 304.** Fracture, at room temperature, of woodflour filled PP. Wood fibres or their impressions determine the appearance of the fracture surface. In the bottom picture, on the left-hand side, two round dots can be seen in the wood fibre (linking passages between wood cells of coniferous wood). (590:1; 1,200:1)

303

304

**305–307.** Ductile fracture in glass fibre reinforced PC. Only a few fibrils are distinguishable in the fracture surface of the amorphous thermoplastic. The dominating feature is convex tear fracture surfaces between the glass fibres. The local direction of failure can be seen from the orientation of the strand pattern (from bottom right to top left). The fine spherical structure could correspond to the basic structure of the polymer. The poor adhesion to the glass fibres is evident from the faulty covering of the exposed fibre ends and the holes in the matrix. (1,000:1; 1,100:1; 11,000:1)

**305**

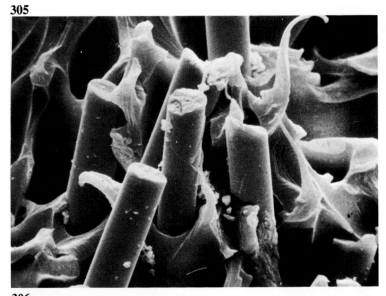

**306**

**307**

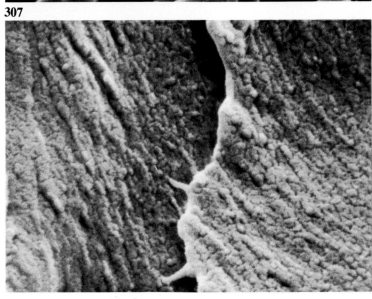

*Polymers with low plastic deformation at break*

Polymers showing poor deformation characteristics (fibre lengths in the fracture 1–10$\mu$m) are, according to our investigations, PS and SAN.

Under conditions which hinder deformation, e.g. high loading rates, low temperatures, multi-axial state of stress and incorporation of foreign materials, normally ductile materials can also fall into this group, e.g. PE, PA, POM, PBTP, PTFE, PC, ABS and PVC.

**308, 309.** Laboratory load fracture of SAN at room temperature. Separation is confined to a layer about 0.15$\mu$m thick (film). Parts of this layer remain attached to one of the fracture surfaces, the rest being attached to the other. During this process, short peaks mostly 1$\mu$m long are formed. Only a few fibrils attain a length of about 20$\mu$m. Minimum fibril thickness 0.1$\mu$m.

The limited ductility is due to the amorphous structure. (2,400:1; 6,000:1)

308

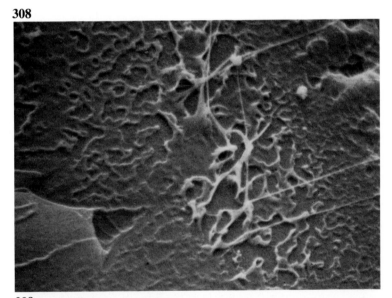

309

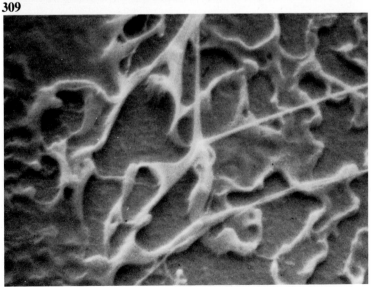

**310, 311.** Laboratory fracture of PVC at room temperature. Because of the poor homogenisation of the raw material there was only limited ductility (cf. **15** and **16**) and only a few fibrils were formed. Maximum fibril length 15μm. (5,000:1; 2,000:1)

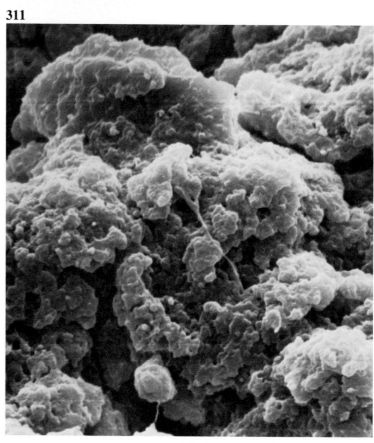

**312, 313.** A laboratory sample of PVC was subjected to repeated tensile stresses. Towards the end of the fatigue fracture, stress and dynamic fatigue fractures alternated periodically in zones a few tenths of a millimetre wide.

Figures **312** and **313** have been taken from two consecutive stress fracture zones. The limited ductility is due to the amorphous structure.

The longest peak in the top photograph measures $8\mu m$, the smallest fibril cross-section is $0.1\mu m$. (2,000:1; 2,000:1)

**312**

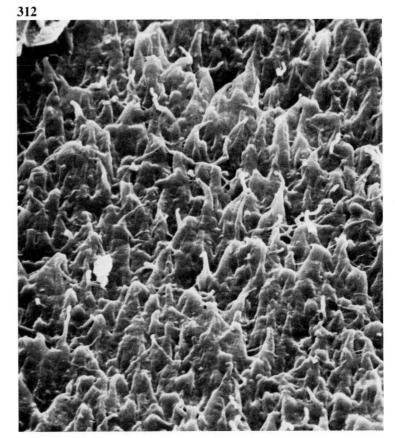

**313**

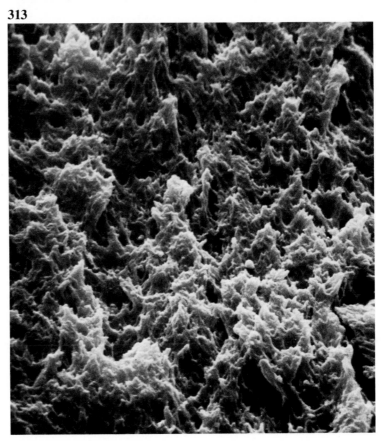

**314, 315.** A high molecular weight HDPE sample was subjected to vibration stresses at room temperature. The fracture has the characteristic features of a ductile material, namely peaks and fibrils (fibril length up to $5\mu$m). The smallest fibril cross-section is $0.01\mu$m. The limited ductility is due to the relatively poor homogeneity of the specimen, which had been compression moulded from granular material (particle size a few tenths of a millimetre, cf. **12–14**). (2,000:1; 10,000:1)

**314**

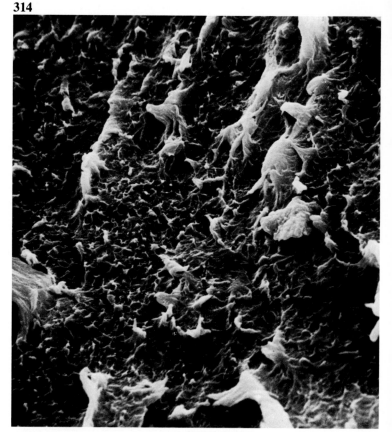

**315**

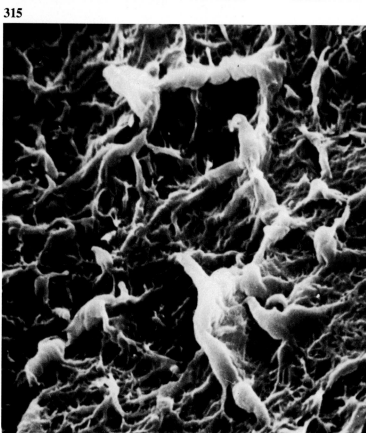

**316–318.** A nylon 6 laboratory sample was subjected to tensile stresses at room temperature until it failed. The curved edge of the initial break, shown in **316**, proves that this is a case of tensile failure. Fracture began roughly in the centre of the sample's flat side, as is evident from the different depths of the surface cracks, and then spread in jerks across the whole area. This is apparent not only in the line-type arrangement of the peaks (line width approximately $10\mu m$) as well as in the transverse striation of the deformation bundles (**318**, band width approximately $1\mu m$). The alignment of the macromolecules in fibrils is seen in the photographs to be from bottom left to top right. The minimum fibril thickness is 0.01mm (**318**). (22:1; 550:1; 2,200:1)

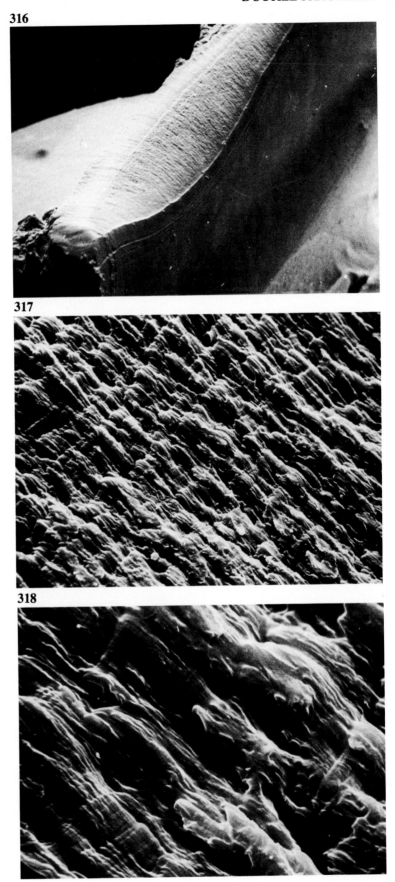

316

317

318

**319, 320.** A nylon 66 laboratory sample was torn. As the tear fracture spread, obliquely slanted peaks remained. The direction of crack propagation is from bottom right to top left in **319**. Maximum fibril length 10$\mu$m, minimum fibril diameter within a closed fibre bundle 0.01mm. (600:1; 6,000:1)

**319**

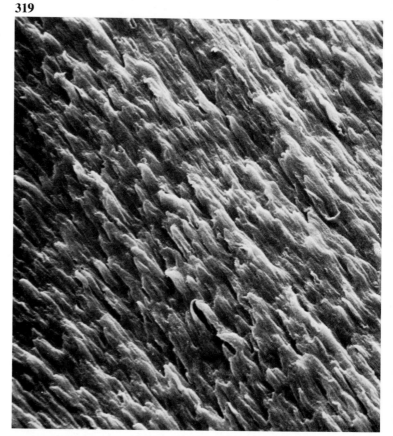

**320**

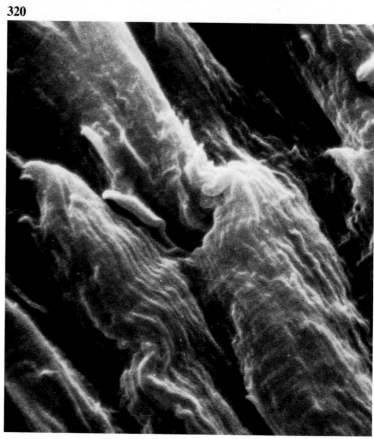

**Brittle fractures.** There is no brittle failure in polymers which could be compared with the cleavage fracture encountered in metals with a body-centred cubic crystal structure. Even with low temperature fractures, ductile deformed films and fibrils become visible at high magnifications, although these deformations are limited to a plane layer less than $1\mu$m thick. Since the deformed volume is very small, one can refer to brittle failure from the macroscopic point of view. Microscopically, one can observe that the stressed, $1\mu$m layer is distributed over the two fracture surfaces after separation, forming oval lids or torn-open blisters, steps and striped patterns. The rims of the microstructures are edged with fine beads and sometimes with short fibrils. Since brittle fractures spread transversely through the material, they leave behind structures which give an indication of the direction of fracture propagation. These are cleavage stops formed where there are inhomogeneities in the material. Here, the fracture front divides into several sections which reunite as the fracture progresses. In this way, step-like patterns are produced, as well as chips which splinter off (**321**).

**321**

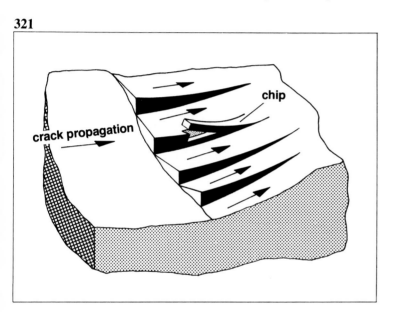

**321.** Formation of cleavage stops (brittle failure bands) when a brittle fracture passes over inhomogeneities. Sometimes chips will splinter off in the process.

Embrittlement at temperatures below the glass transition point (**7**) is called ageing. It is related to an increase in density and can be eliminated by heating above the glass transition temperature, followed by quenching*, provided no cracks have begun to appear.

Another embrittling influence is UV radiation which is likewise related to a density increase.

*Brittle fractures at room temperature*
According to our definition, deformation with fibrils about $1\mu$m long or less mean brittle fracture. This type of fracture was observed in PBTP, POM, PE, PVC, PC, PS, SAN, ABS, EP and glass fibre reinforced polyester.

*Gräfen, H. and Morbitzer, L. (Personal communication).

**322, 323.** Laboratory fracture of PS at room temperature. The fracture began with a craze on the narrow face of the sample (**322**, bottom left) and propagated from the bottom towards the top. The characteristic features are level brittle failure bands and splintering chips.

The micro-structure of the film zone can be seen in **325**. (24:1; 120:1)

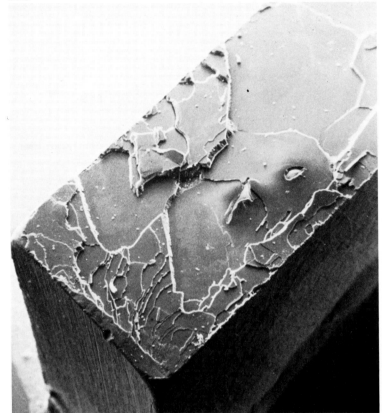

**324, 325.** Brittle fracture of PS at room temperature. Deformation during fracture is confined to a film about $0.25\mu$m thick. The pulled-up deformation beads, too, remain in this order of magnitude. The fracture spread in a direction parallel to the brittle failure bands (**324**), from the bottom to the top. Over a large area the film was not distributed over the two fracture surfaces, so that the traces of separation only left a roughness of about $0.1\mu$m. (600:1; 6,000:1)

**324**

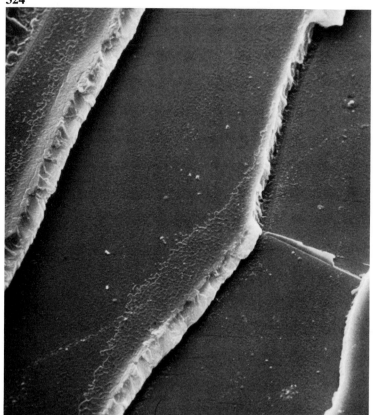

**325**

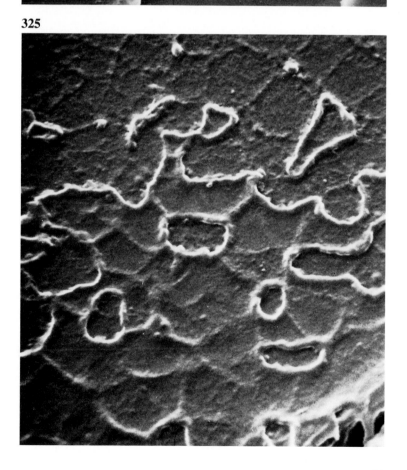

**326, 327.** Brittle fracture of SAN at room temperature. Deformation is confined to a layer $0.25\mu$m thick. The fracture spread into several planes. Direction of fracture propagation from the bottom upwards. (1,000:1; 5,000:1)

**326**

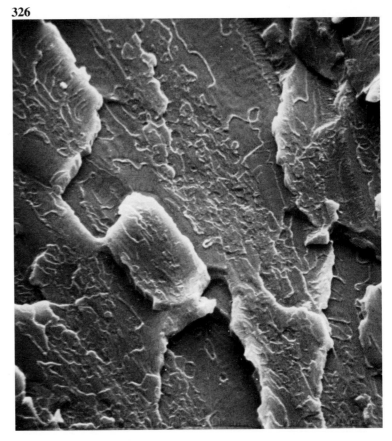

**327**

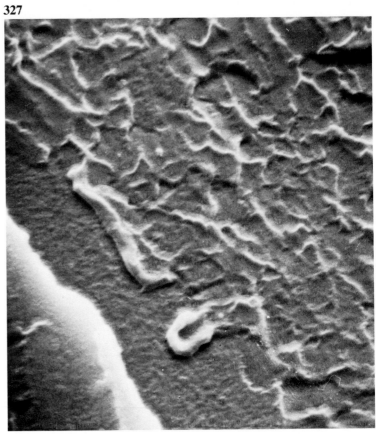

**328, 329.** A laboratory sample of ABS was stressed with 29.4N/mm² at room temperature and failed after 27 minutes. There was little external constriction and the deformation was absorbed by the micro-structure. Very flat peaks and dimple structures do not exceed 0.5μm. The macroscopically brittle fracture may be regarded as micro-ductile. The size of the holes corresponds to the size of the butadiene rubber particles. (2,400:1; 12,000:1)

328

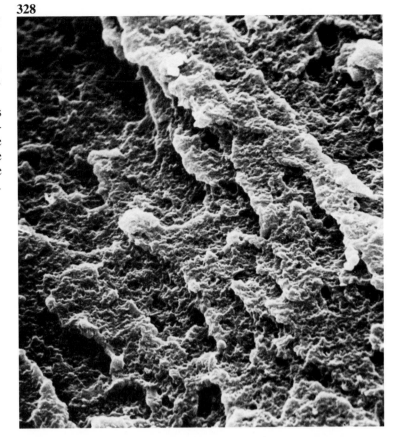

329

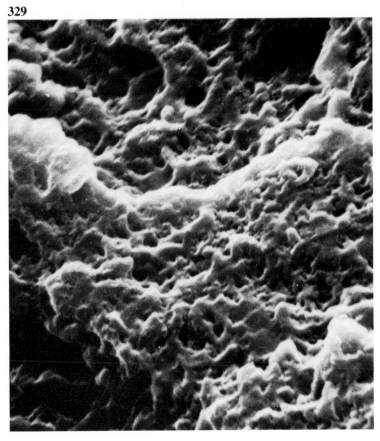

**330, 331.** Brittle fracture produced in PC at room temperature in the laboratory, the PC previously having been subjected to outdoor weathering. Abrupt fracture propagation along a wide front, from the bottom upwards. The structures may be explained by the pulling-up and tearing of film strips. (240:1; 2,400:1)

**330**

**331**

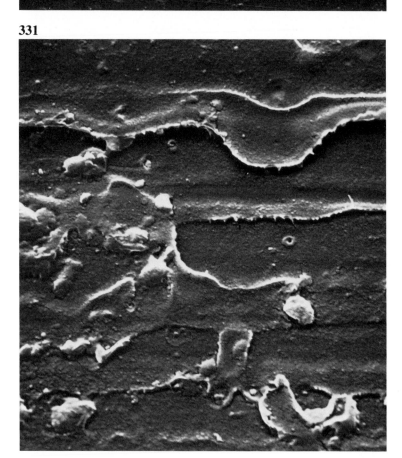

**332, 333.** HDPE of a bottle crate after being in use and exposed to the elements for nine years. The surface which has been most affected by embrittlement showed a pattern of cracks (top left in **332**). Characteristic features of embrittlement: smooth fracture surfaces divided into bands by steps. Height of peaks 0.1µm max. (260:1; 13,000:1)

**332**

**333**

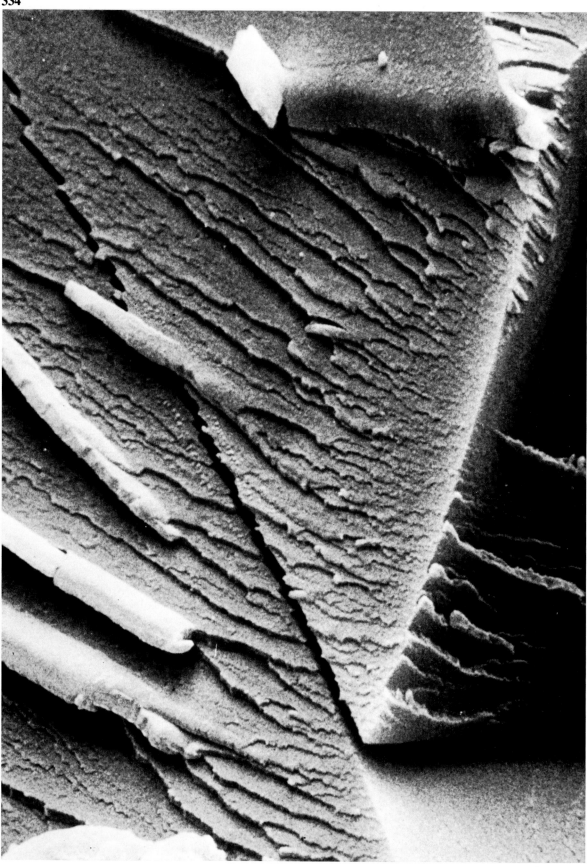

**334–337.** Brittle fracture of PBTP at room temperature. Fracture propagation from the bottom upwards. In many parallel brittle fracture bands hardly any traces of deformation can be recognised. Troughs and peaks remain in the order of magnitude of $0.1\mu$m (**337**). Characteristic features of brittle failure also include splinters (**336**). (3,200:1; 220:1; 2,200:1; 11,000:1)

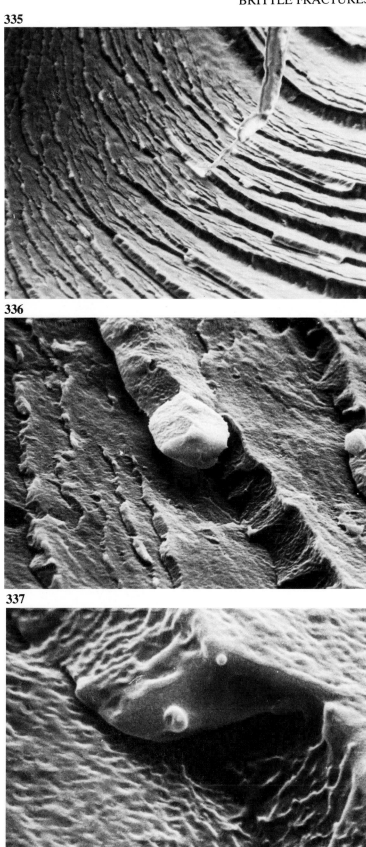

335

336

337

**338, 339.** Fracture produced in glass fibre reinforced PP at room temperature (30% w/w glass).

The polymer showed very good adhesion to the glass fibres so that their free ends were covered with PP residues after fracture. The fracture in the polymer is due to brittle failure. Isolated peaks have lengths of up to 1μm. (550:1; 2,200:1)

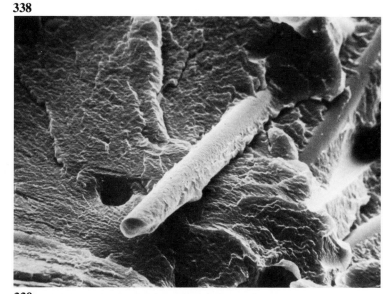

338

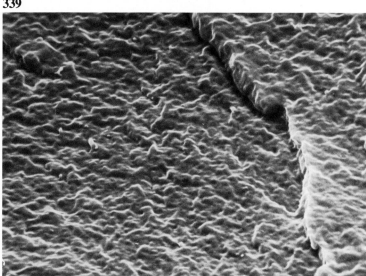

339

**340.** Fracture produced in glass fibre reinforced PP at room temperature (30% w/w glass).

The PP shows brittle fracture. Because of poor adhesion between the polymer and the glass fibres, there is no residual PP on the glass surfaces. Accordingly, the impressions of the glass fibres in the PP have smooth surfaces. (600:1)

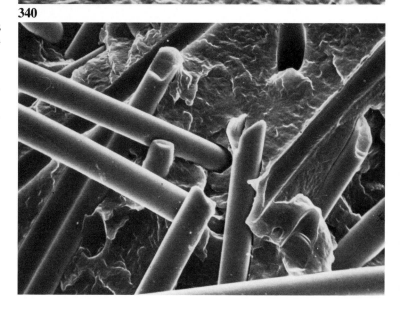

340

**341**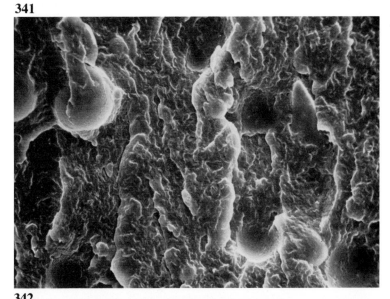

**341.** Brittle fracture produced in nylon 6 with 30% glass beads, at room temperature. Most of the glass beads became detached from the fracture surface during fracture, due to their poor adhesion. (600:1)

**342**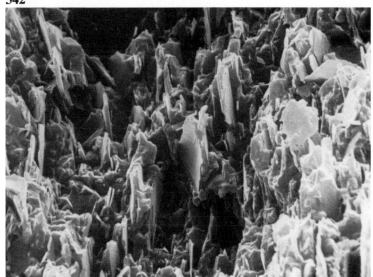

**342.** Fracture produced in nylon 6 with 30% talc, at room temperature. The talc flakes determine the appearance of the fracture surface. (2,400:1)

**343**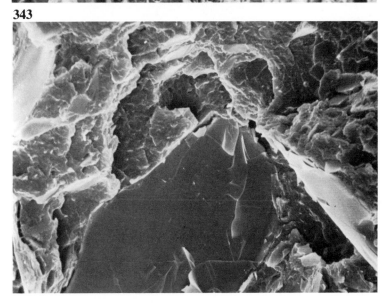

**343.** Fracture produced in nylon 6 with 30% mica, at room temperature. The brittle fracture is oriented along the flat, smooth mica platelets. (600:1)

**344, 345.** Fracture produced in EP at room temperature. The fracture spread mostly from the bottom upwards. Local deviations from this main direction are evident from the brittle fracture paths edged by pale areas. There is a feathery texture within the fracture paths. (120:1; 2,600:1)

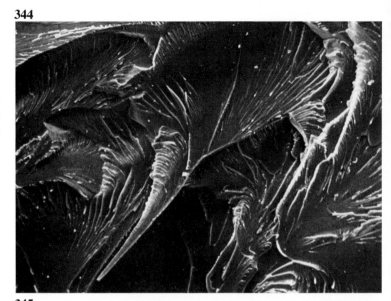

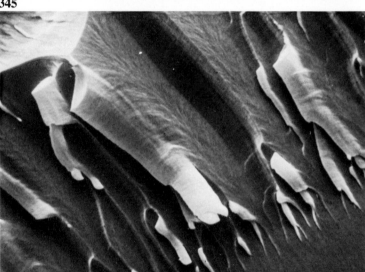

**346.** Fracture in polyester resin, produced at room temperature. The fracture spread from the bottom upwards, along brittle fracture paths. A feathery pattern can be seen on these paths and chips have splintered off at the edges of the brittle fracture paths. (2,100:1)

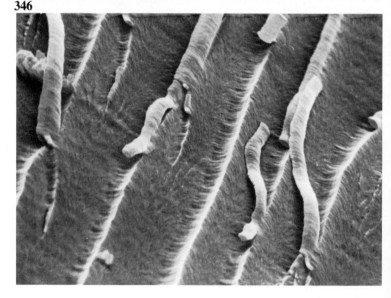

**347.** Brittle fracture in the matrix of a glass fibre reinforced polyester resin sample. Feathery texture, fracture propagation from bottom left to top right. (6,000:1)

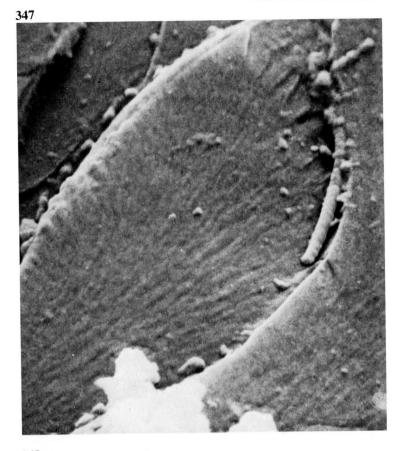

**348.** The same sample as in **347**. The U-shaped ramp shows the fracture propagation from right to left. (6,500:1)

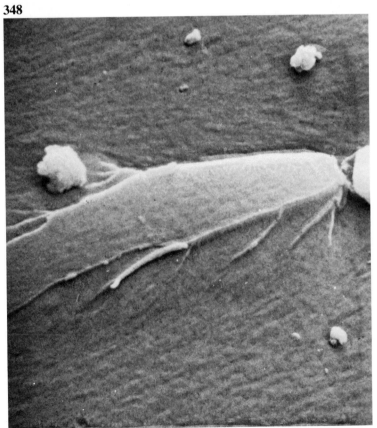

**349, 350.** Fracture in PF resin filled with cotton fibres, produced at room temperature. The cotton fibres only slightly prevented spreading of the brittle fracture. The fracture spread from top left to bottom right and left behind a feathery pattern on the brittle fracture bands. Chips splintered off at the edges of the brittle fracture bands. (1,200:1; 5,200:1)

**349**

**350**

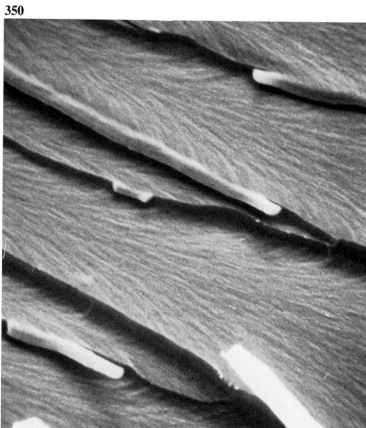

## Brittle fractures at low temperatures

According to our definition that ductile deformation with fibrils less than 1μm long mean brittle fracture, all the polymeric materials examined by us will produce this type of fracture at −170°C, as expected. The following materials were examined: POM, PA 66. PE, PVC, PS, glass fibre reinforced PC and EP.

**351–353.** Brittle fracture in PVC at —170°C. Fracture propagation from the bottom upwards in **351**. The micro-characteristics are areas and peaks separated by steps, around the spherical polymerisation structures whose height is less than 0.2μm. (55:1; 550:1; 5,500:1)

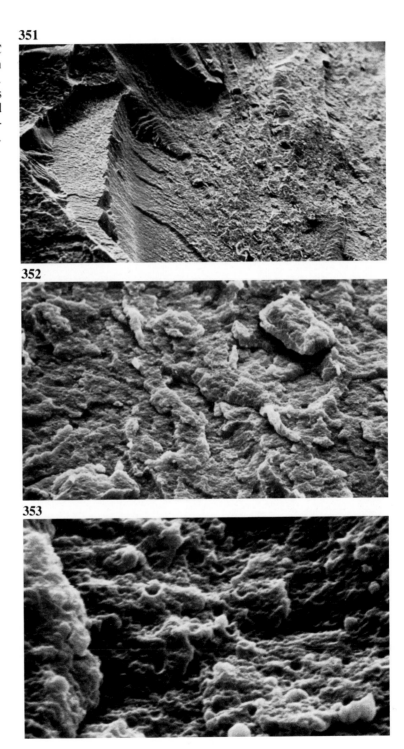

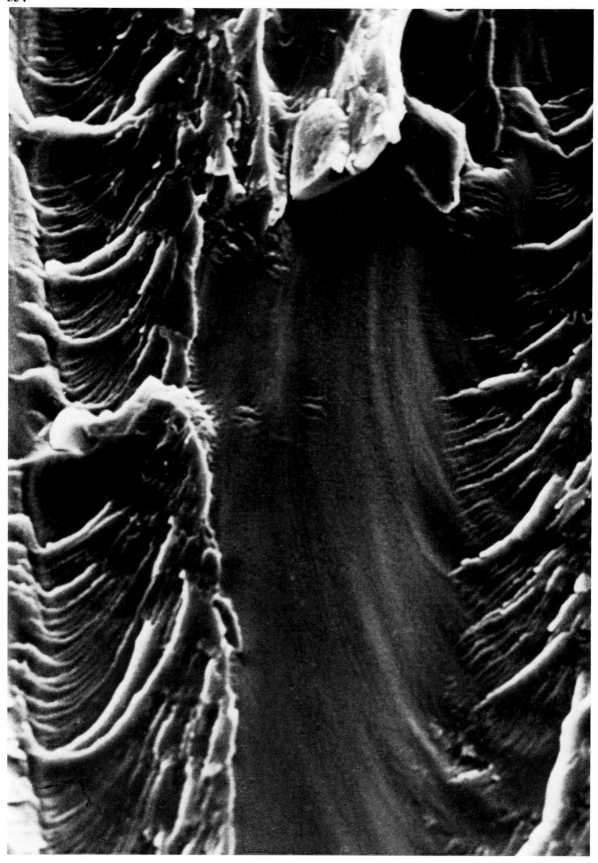

**354, 355.** Brittle fracture in PVC at —170°C. Fracture propagation in both pictures from top right to bottom left. The micro-characteristics consist of many parallel fracture paths which combine in the direction of crack propagation. Concentric beach marks lie at right angles to the bands. (600:1; 220:1)

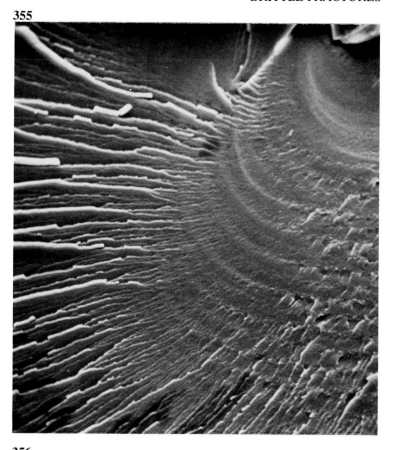

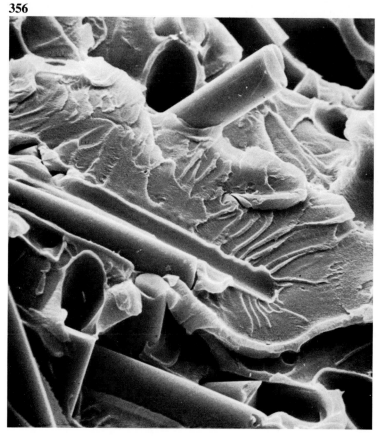

**356.** Brittle fracture produced in glass fibre reinforced PC at —170°C. The characteristic features are concave areas with a fine, knot-like structure and short peaks at the edges of the areas (mean peak length 0.4μm). (1,050:1)

**357, 358.** Brittle fracture produced in glass fibre reinforced PC at —170°C. The characteristic features are concave areas with a fine, knot-like structure and peaks at the edges of these areas. (10,500:1; 21,000:1)

**357**

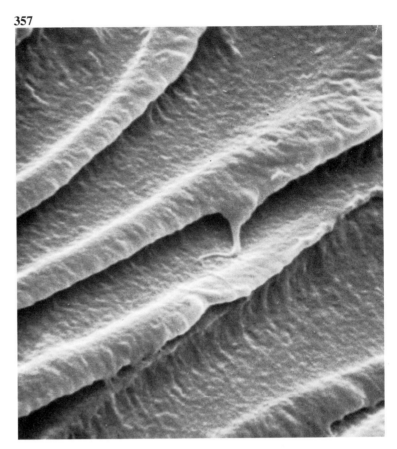

**358**

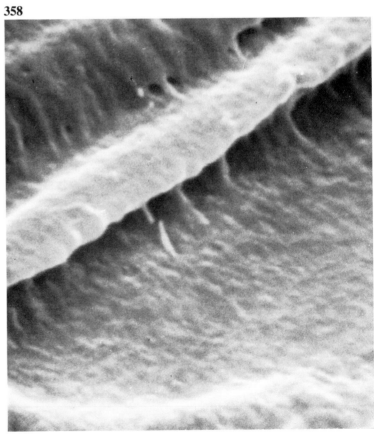

**359, 360.** Brittle fracture in PE at —170°C. Fracture propagation from bottom left to top right in **359**. The characteristic feature is fine micro-peaks (about 0.1μm high). (550:1; 11,000:1)

**359**

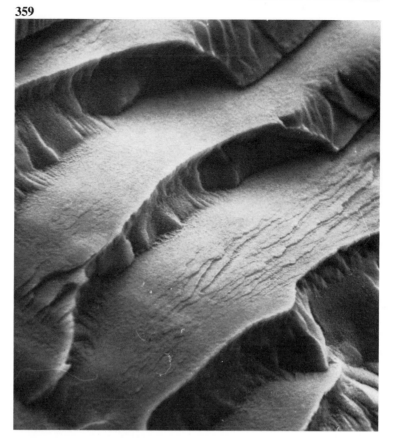

**360**

**361.** Brittle fracture in POM at −170°C. The fracture propagated from bottom right to top left. Deformation was limited to a 0.25μm thick film. (2,400:1)

**361**

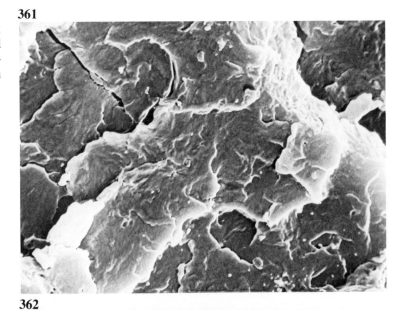

**362**

**362, 363.** Brittle fracture in POM at −170°C. Fracture propagation from the bottom upwards. Hardly any traces of deformation can be distinguished on the many brittle fracture paths. The fracture has exposed a porosity of the material (**363**; cf. **62** and **63**). (600:1; 2,400:1)

**363**

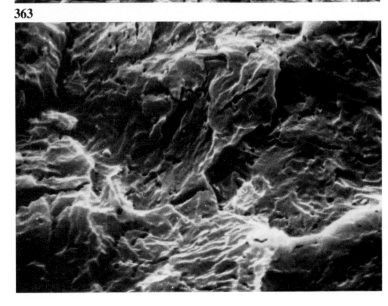

**364, 365.** Fracture produced in epoxy resin at —170°C. The fracture surface is characterised by many pin-point crazes within the material. From these, brittle fractures propagate radially until they combine with the adjacent cracks. Chips have splintered off along the brittle fracture paths. (600:1; 1,200:1)

**364**

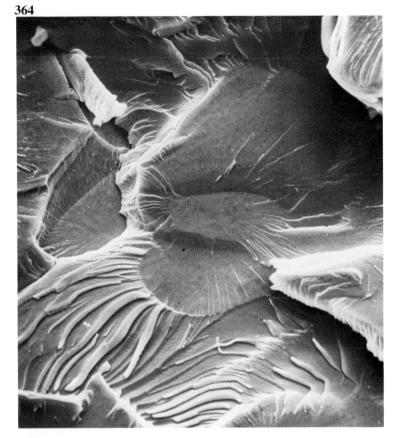

**365**

# DYNAMIC FATIGUE FRACTURES

Like other materials, polymers are far less capable of withstanding vibrational stresses than static ones. The number of load cycles which a material can withstand increases with decreasing alternating stress. The curves showing the relationship between alternating flexural stress and number of load cycles therefore tend to flatten out (**366**).

**366**

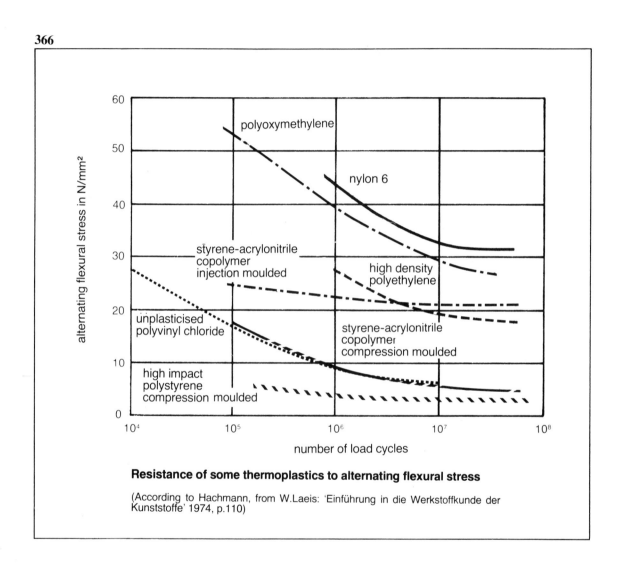

**Resistance of some thermoplastics to alternating flexural stress**

(According to Hachmann, from W.Laeis: 'Einführung in die Werkstoffkunde der Kunststoffe' 1974, p.110)

**Vibration-induced creep fractures.** True resistance to long-term vibration would be possible only if the alternating stress were to be absorbed permanently and purely elastically. This would only be possible, however, if largely elastic behaviour were found also in the micro-range. One must, however, realise that irreversible stretching processes will occur near heterogeneities on the surface or inside the material. This is accompanied by the development of heat which again increases the mobility of the molecule chains. This is why polymers exhibit a form of fatigue fracture which may be said to be equivalent to continuous creep fracture (**367** and **368**). We call this vibration-induced creep fracture. Because of the poor thermal conductivity, vibration-induced creep fracture is also dependent on frequency. High frequencies and high loads involve the risk of local softening and even melting at the centre of the cross-sectional area. In this case one cannot reckon on signs of a periodic progress of the crack in the fracture surface, i.e. there will be no striations.

If there are sure signs of fatigue fracture such as striations, fatigue crack paths, secondary cracks or spherical melt cavities, vibration fracture can be positively identified. It is also possible, however, for vibration stresses to leave behind only signs of force fracture. Fatigue fractures with striations are particularly common in very ductile polymers, at high operating temperatures and high load cycle frequencies. It would be theoretically possible to have a vibration fracture with extreme fracture constriction and point-like or edge-like separation. Normally, a much rounded surface crack will migrate from the surface or from an internal fault, through the material (**369**).

**367**

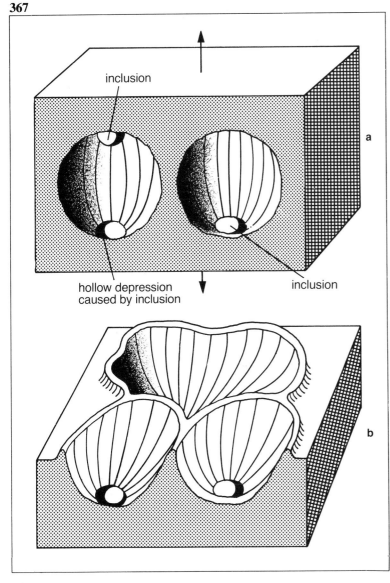

inclusion

a

hollow depression
caused by inclusion

inclusion

b

**367.** When a polymeric material is heated too much by vibrations, many cavities are formed which assume a more or less spherical shape due to stretching. After separation, funnel-shaped depressions or semi-spherical structures with raised edges remain behind in the fracture surface.

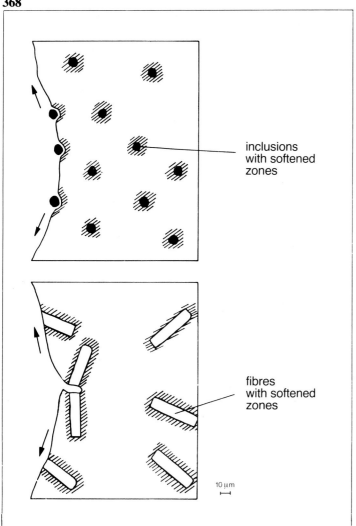

inclusions
with softened
zones

fibres
with softened
zones

10 μm

**368.** The vibration-induced creep fracture exposes inclusions and fillers deposited in the smooth fracture surface by a surrounding cavity. Large included particles, e.g. glass fibres, are broken through smoothly.

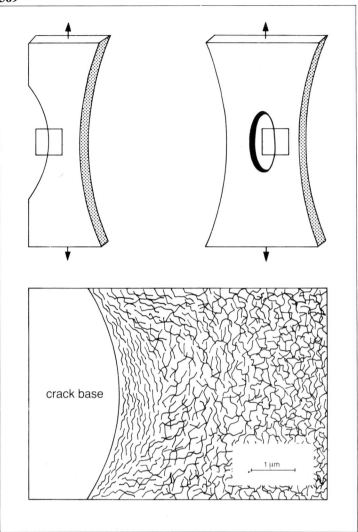

crack base

1 μm

**369.** Ductile fatigue fracture without fatigue striations. Strongly rounded crack base. Crack propagation continuously through spreading of a stretched zone. There is no sharp crack tip. In soft polymers there is no recognisable fracture propagation for every load change and one can only distinguish the characteristic features of a static ductile fracture.

**370.** A vibration-induced creep fracture was produced within the cross-section of a PS sample. A brittle residual fracture occurred towards the outside. The characteristic features of creep fracture can only be seen at greater magnification. (24:1)

**370**

**371**

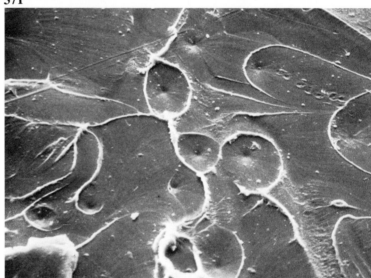

**371, 372.** Vibration-induced creep fracture in PS. Voids have been formed at the centre of the sample cross-section (**370**), whose edges stretched under considerable elongation. Separation occurred through joining-up of the voids and tearing of the walls in between (see **369**). Inclusions formed the starting points of separation. (550:1; 2,200:1)

**372**

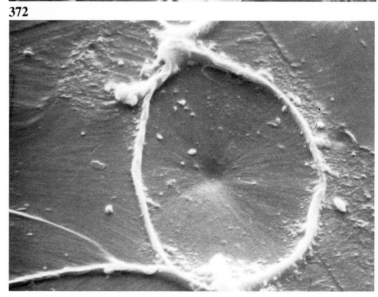

**373–375.** Vibration stress produced fatigue fracture in this SB sample, which started from opposite sides. In the initial stages, paths can be distinguished, but only indications of striations. In fact, vibration-induced creep fracture seems here to predominate, and can be recognised from the softened zones around the included rubber particles (**375**, bottom). Generally, a flat dimple structure is formed analogous to the model shown in **367**. (21:1; 525:1; 5,250:1)

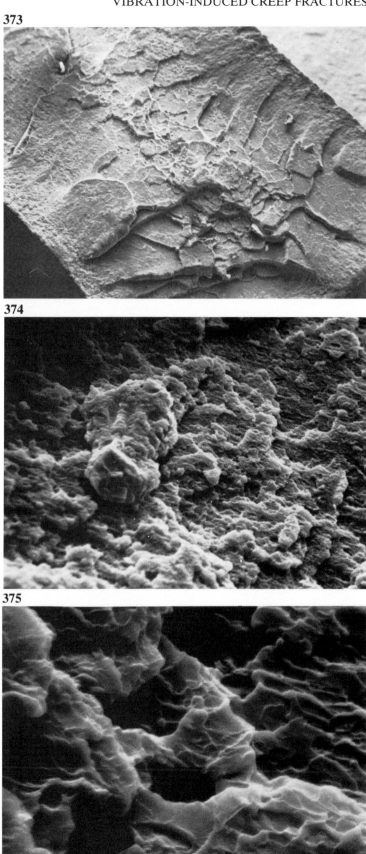

373

374

375

**376, 377.** A PBTP sample, subjected to the alternating bending test failed after 4,381,900 load cycles. The vibration caused softened centres to be formed, in which voids formed as shown in the model (**367**), which then expanded. This produced the blister and rosette patterns. In the immediate vicinity of the blisters, peak-like shapes prove the material's ductility as a result of applied heat. (55:1; 550:1)

**376**

**377**

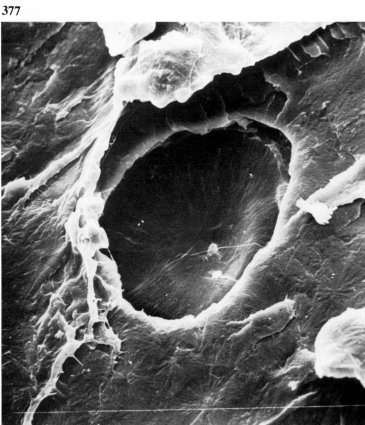

**378, 379.** A vibration stressed PBTP sample failed after 468,000 load cycles. The marked constriction (**378**) was encouraged by the heat produced. A void at the centre of the cross-section shows clear melt structures (**379**). The residual cross-sections near the circumference of the sample were stretched in jerky sliding processes (**379**, top left). (22:1; 110:1)

**378**

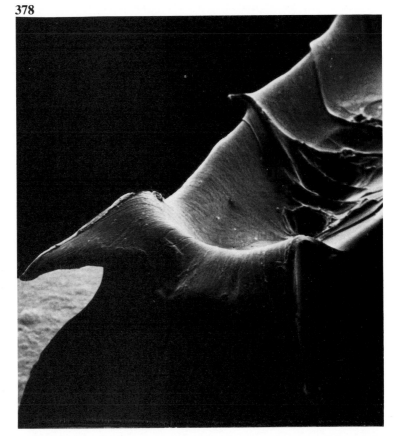

**379**

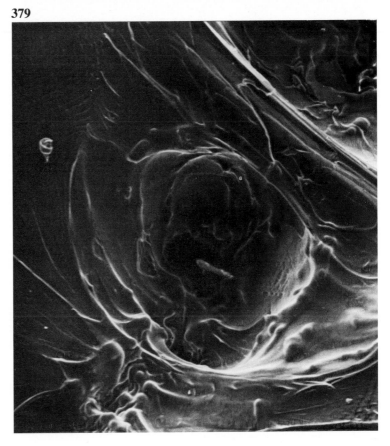

**380.** Vibration-induced melt symptoms in a POM roller. The alternating compressive stresses produced so much heat in the region of maximum shear stress underneath the surface that the material melted, and exuded from the side of the roller. (24:1)

**380**

**381.** Vibration fracture in POM, whose symptoms should rather be classified as those of vibration-induced creep fracture. This is evident from the rounded forms which indicate softening. (5,000:1)

**381**

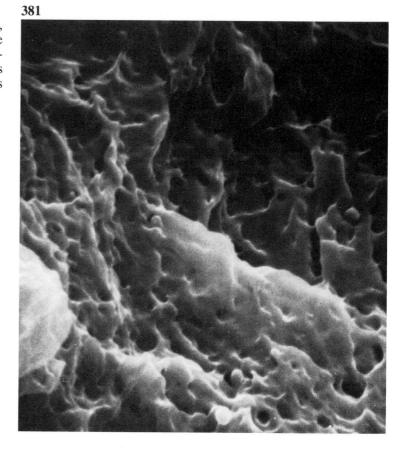

**382, 383.** A hose was subjected to long term alternating bending which caused the viscose fibres to become warm and caused a vibration-induced creep fracture to be propagated. (2,000:1; 2,000:1)

**382**

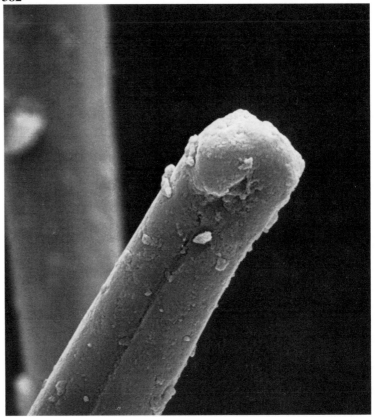

**383**

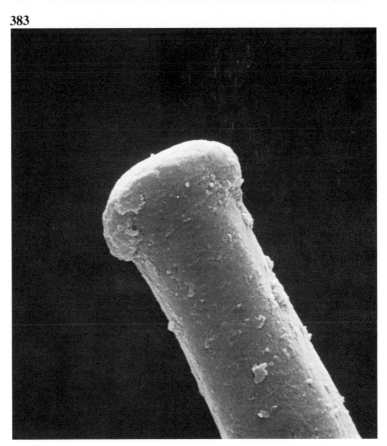

**384, 385.** Vibration-induced creep fracture in glass fibre reinforced PP (30% w/w glass). Heat accumulation is concentrated around the fibres and is apparent from softened haloes with stretch patterns and raised edges around the fibre cross-sections (see also **301** and **302**). The small filler inclusions, too, are surrounded by haloes and raised edges. The glass fibres are broken through smoothly, in contrast to normal load fracture (see also **302**), because they are completely surrounded during fracture by the matrix, which shows good adhesion to them. In **385** ductile creep deformation is shown by two clear peak-like structures. (1,200:1; 1,200:1)

**384**

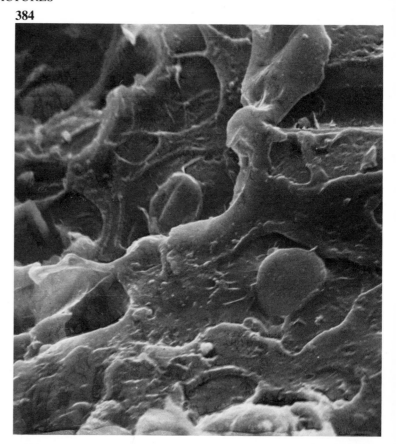

**385**

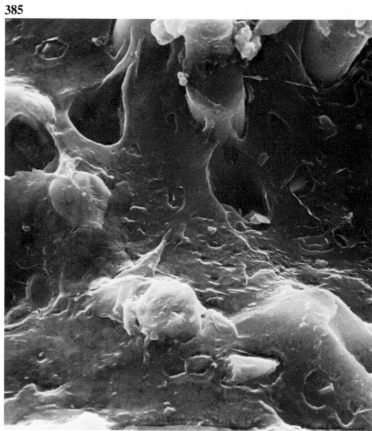

**386, 387.** Vibration-induced creep fracture in a PVC sample. At the origin of the fracture, a fibrous pattern was formed, due to numerous fracture bands. At the end of the fracture (**388**) the fracture progressed in jerks as a tear load fracture. (22:1; 600:1)

**386**

**387**

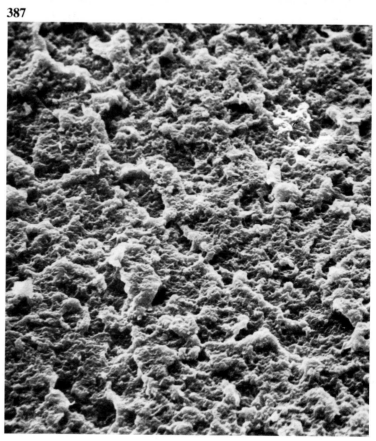

**388, 389.** The characteristic features of vibration-induced creep fracture in PVC are fracture paths and exposed primary polymerisation structures (see also **15–18**). The particle in the middle of **389**, for example, is composed of several individual primary particles. The dimple structure has a certain similarity with force fractures from which, however, it differs when compared in detail (cf. **313**). The rounded fracture forms indicate that heat was developed near the crack tip. (2,400:1; 500:1)

**388**

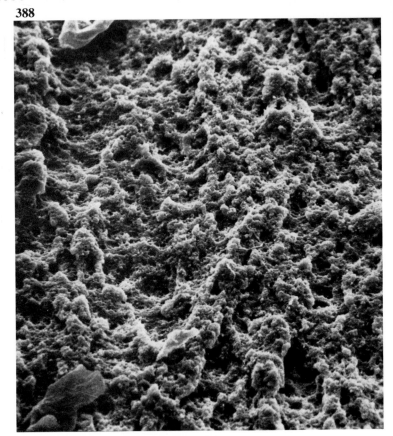

**389**

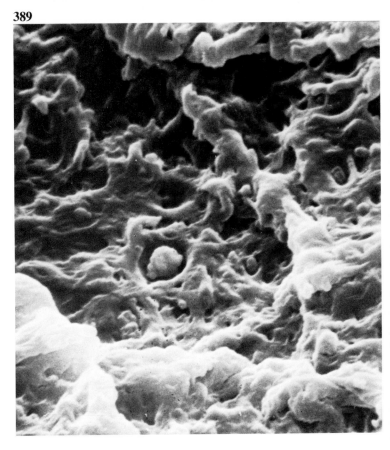

**True vibration fractures.** In materials which are difficult to deform, application of alternating stresses will produce a true crack tip. Because of the spatial rigidity of the molecular bonds, the molecule chains are separated by the crack tip after only slight stretching (**390**). A crack front with a sharply defined notch can be formed and migrate through the polymer under alternating loads, with the formation of parallel fatigue striations. This phenomenon depends not only on the material but also on the load frequency and the extent of loading. True vibration fractures have been observed in PC, SAN, PVC, PE, PA and PP.

One can distinguish between more or less deformed striations according to the possible deformation until separation occurs at the base of the crack.

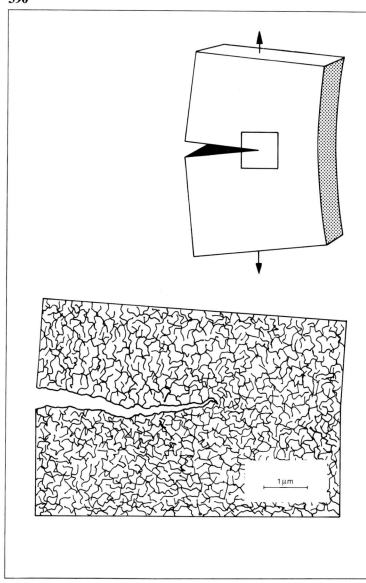

**390.** Vibration fracture in polymeric materials with fatigue striations. The molecule chains are separated after slight stretching.

## True ductile fatigue cracks

Materials that are relatively easy to deform, produce crease-like and rounded, flap-like fractures between the continuous cracks (**391**). The fatigue striations, too, tend to be fold-like and rounded, and inclusions lie exposed in the crack.

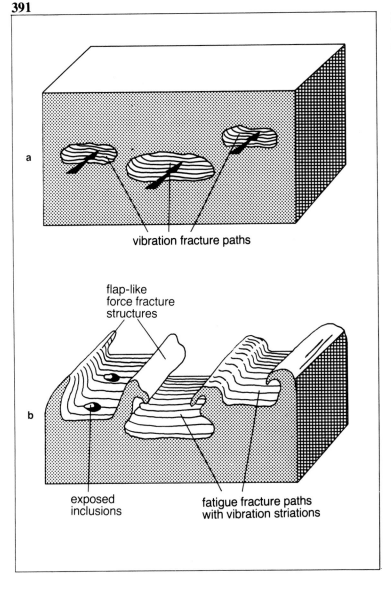

**391.** Propagation of fatigue fracture within staggered fatigue striations in ductile polymers.

a

vibration fracture paths

flap-like
force fracture
structures

b

exposed
inclusions

fatigue fracture paths
with vibration striations

**392, 393.** Fatigue fracture in a sample of high molecular weight HDPE. The fracture centre lies beneath the surface and the fracture propagation in paths can be clearly seen from the radial fibrous marks. (20:1; 220:1)

**392**

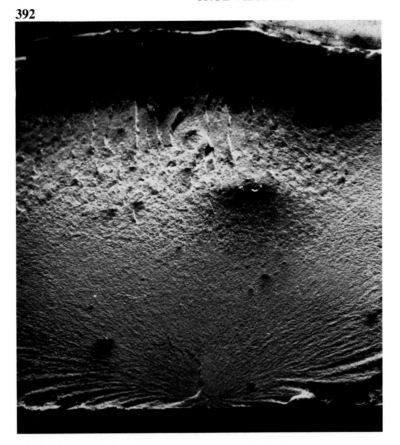

**393**

**394, 395.** The end of a fatigue fracture in a sample of high molecular weight HDPE. The fracture spread in paths and left behind ductile striations and secondary cracks. The paths are separated from each other by flap-like force fractures (see also **387**). (200:1; 1,000:1)

**394**

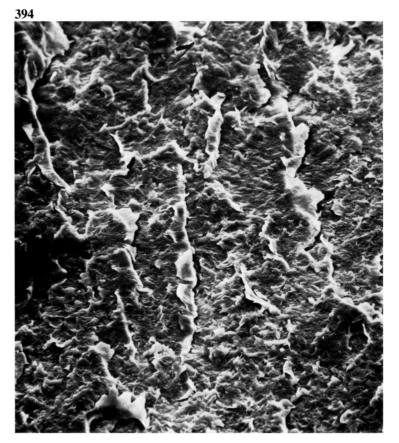

**395**

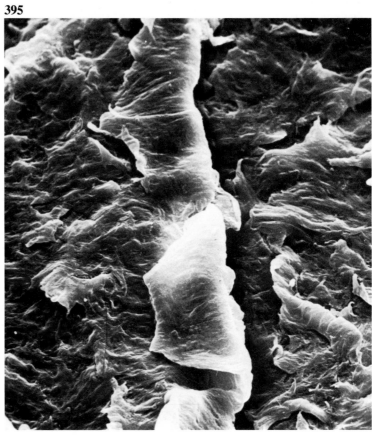

**396, 397.** A POM sample failed after 18,270 load cycles. The centre of the fatigue fracture is a craze arranged around a bubble. The characteristic features of a fatigue fracture are fracture paths with striations and isolated secondary cracks. (22:1; 525:1)

396

397

**398, 399.** The dynamic fatigue fracture (from **396**) presumably exposed spherulitic structures (diameter a few tenths of a $\mu$m). Striations can be seen only at the end of the fracture (**399**). (5,000:1; 5,250:1)

**398**

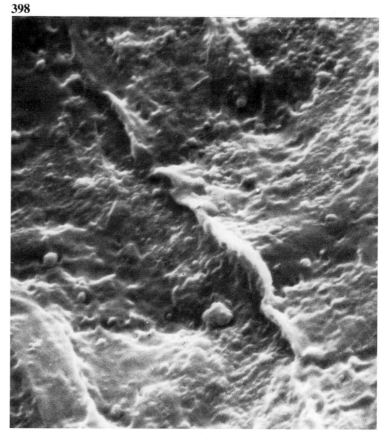

**399**

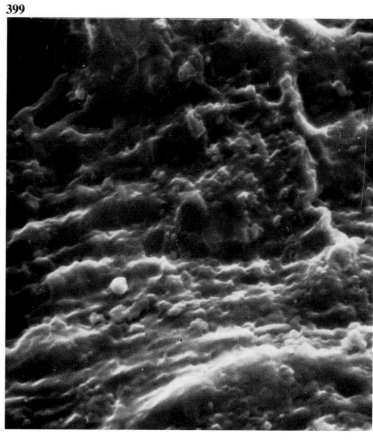

**400, 401.** The dynamic fatigue fracture in a POM sample propagated in paths. Lattice-type stretched areas of the material, which was already porous before, can be seen in the flap-like fractures between the bands. The surface of the paths has been rounded by heat (see also **62** and **63**). (2,000:1; 5,000:1)

**400**

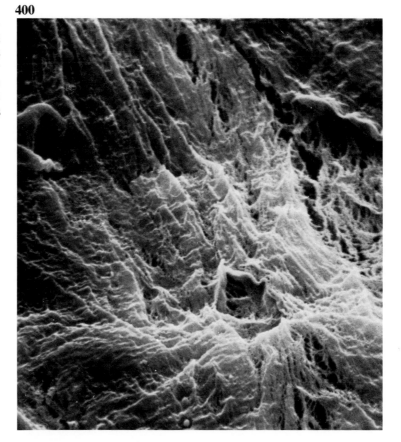

**401**

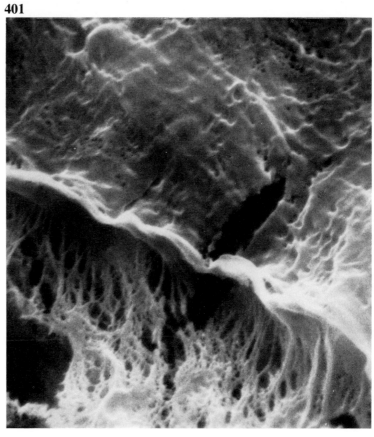

**402.** Dynamic fatigue fracture in a nylon 66 sample. The fracture spreads out in paths and leaves behind ductile striations and secondary cracks. Flap-like separations limit the fracture paths. (2,000:1)

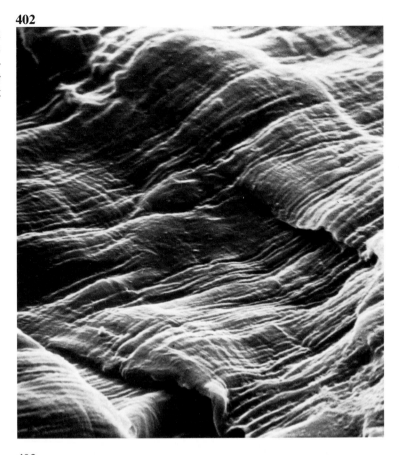

**403.** A compression moulded nylon 6 sample failed after 1,295,700 load cycles. The fracture spread in paths and left behind numerous secondary cracks. The striations are poorly defined. The rounded structures are due to spherulites for which particularly favourable conditions exist during compression moulding. (1,800:1)

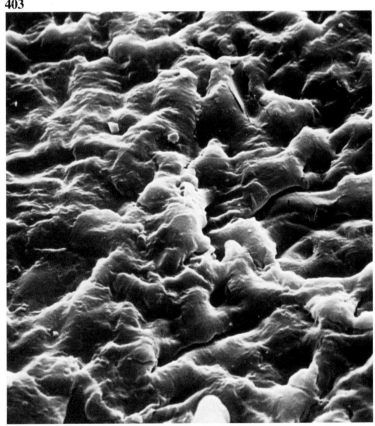

**404**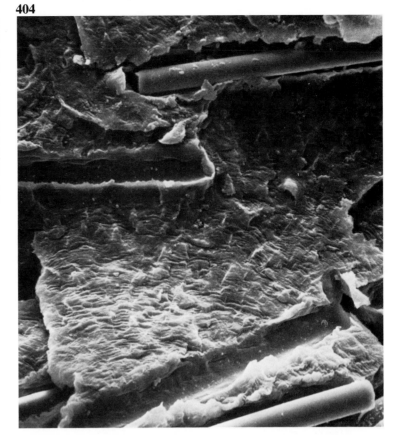

**404, 405.** Ductile fatigue fracture in a glass fibre reinforced nylon 6 sample (9% w/w glass fibre). The characteristic features of dynamic fatigue fractures are fronts of striations. These were left by the vibration fracture whilst it spread from glass fibre to glass fibre. The rounded, creased striations and the flap-like boundaries between partial fractures (e.g. bottom left in **405**) are signs of ductile fatigue fracture. As a comparison see also the fracture in **297** and **298**. (600:1; 2,400:1)

**405**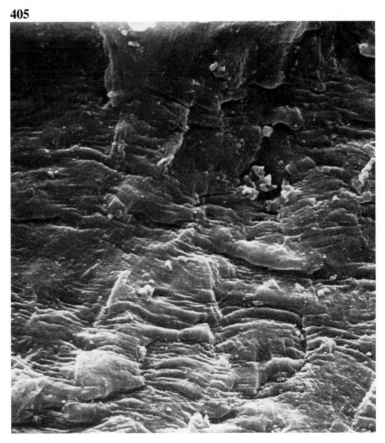

### True brittle fatigue cracks

In polymers which are very difficult to deform, striations with very flat profiles and sharp-edged steps between the paths are formed (**406**).

As the fatigue crack is spreading in the form of a crack front, inclusions act as obstacles. Hard inclusions are 'climbed over' by the crack front, so that they become visible in the fracture surface, either exposed or covered. Soft inclusions are cut through by the sharp-edged crack root. With these characteristic features, the brittle fatigue cracks in polymers bear the closest resemblance to fatigue cracks in metals.

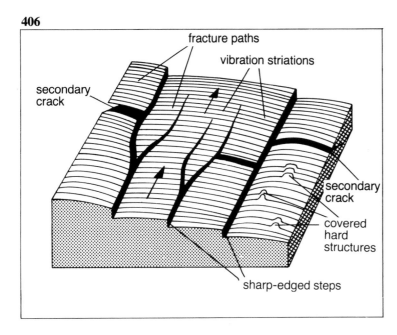

**406**

**406.** Fatigue fracture in brittle polymers, with fatigue fracture paths limited by sharp edges, striations and secondary cracks. The arrows indicate the direction of crack propagation.

**407, 408.** Brittle fatigue fracture in press moulded SAN after 180,000 load cycles. Sharp-edged fracture bands produce a radial, fibrous pattern. Some beach marks have formed at right angles to the fibrous marks. After the fatigue fracture there is a jerkily progressing, brittle force fracture (**407**).

The characteristic features of brittle fatigue fracture are as follows: sharp-edged paths and striations with flat, low-deformation profiles. (50:1; 2,000:1)

407

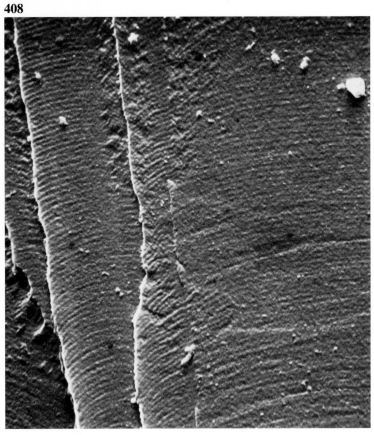

408

**409, 410.** An SAN sample failed after 76,500 load cycles through vibration fracture. The fracture spread along sharp-edged paths from a fault inside the sample, forming radial, concentric fracture fronts. Only the circular, smooth area shows signs of fatigue fracture. Outside the circular area there is a brittle stress fracture. Although the fatigue fracture paths with sharp edges are very clearly defined at the start (**409**), only traces of striations can be discerned. Another feature of brittle fatigue fracture is the inclusions which are seen to be covered in the photograph. (23:1; 5,750:1)

**409**

**410**

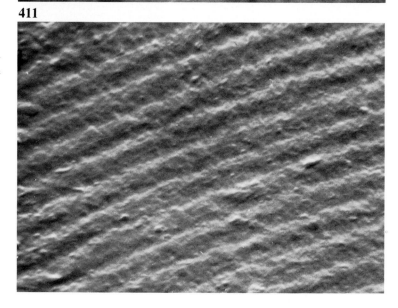

**411.** At the end (this is from the edge of the circular area in **409**) the fatigue fracture spread in sharp-edged paths. At right angles to these there are clearly defined, but flat, striations. (5,500:1)

**411**

**412.** The brittle fatigue fracture in SB with incorporated rubber particles (diameter 1–3$\mu$m) started at the surface and spread radially through the cross-section. The numerous sharp-edged fracture paths produced a fibrous pattern. The sharp-edged crack front cut through the butadiene particles. (1,100:1)

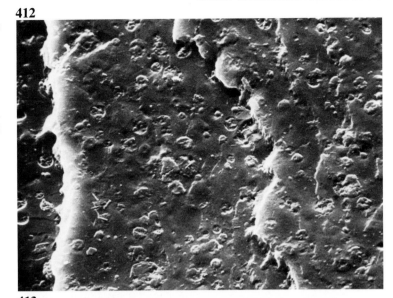

**413, 414.** The characteristic features of brittle fatigue fracture (from **412**) in the PS matrix are:

– sharp-edged fracture paths in the PS

  – striations in the PS

  – secondary cracks in the PS

  – covered primary structures

  – cut-through, soft inclusions consisting of coherent rubber compound with incorporated PS particles (diameter 0.1–0.5$\mu$m). (5,250:1; 10,500:1)

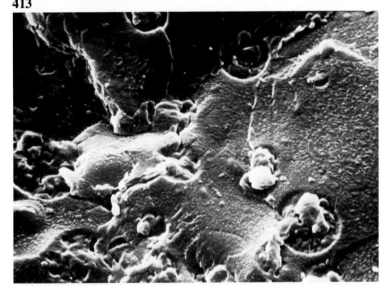

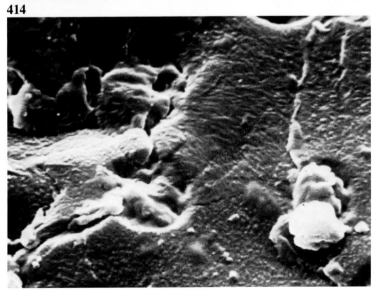

**415, 416.** Brittle fatigue fracture in an ABS sample after 497,000 load cycles. In this poorly defined fatigue fracture the fracture paths are the essential features. The absence of lips, peaks and films in the fracture surfaces proves that this is not a static stress fracture. (220:1; 11,000:1)

**415**

**416**

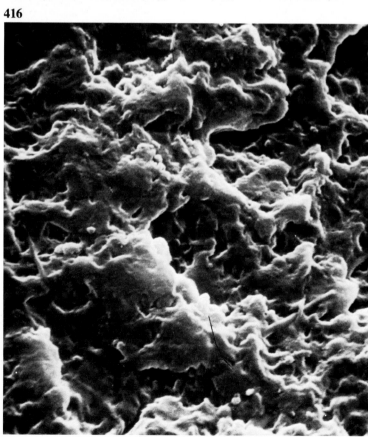

**417–419.** The crack in a clutch coupling made of nylon 6 was broken open. Sharp-edged steps in the fracture zone show a brittle fatigue fracture which started out from the surface. This cut through the spherulites present in the material, as it spread. The beach marks, which indicate the former crack front, therefore pass over the structural characteristics. A porous shrinkage structure can be seen within the spherulites (**419**, cf. also **62** and **63**). (100:1; 2,000:1; 10,000:1)

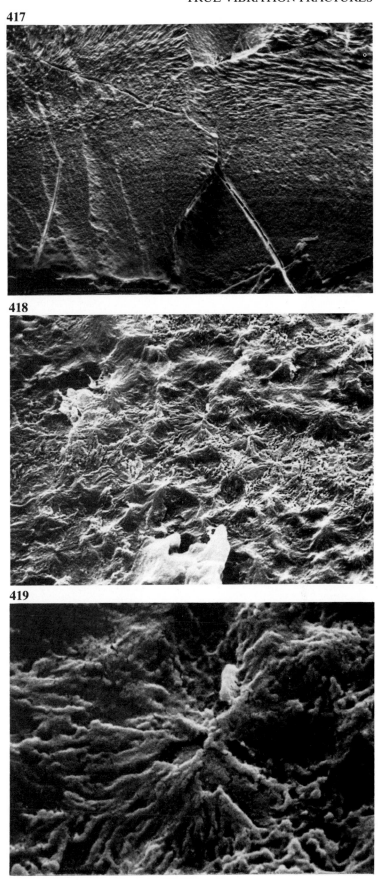

417

418

419

**420, 421.** Glass fibre reinforced polyester sample which had failed under repeated tensile stress. Long sections of glass fibre had been exposed due to vibration stresses, leaving a matrix perforated by tubes and voids. In the resin itself mainly low-deformation fractures were observed. The characteristic features of dynamic fatigue fracture are long bundles of glass fibres protruding from the fracture surface. Resin residues adhere to these bundles. This does not occur if an identical sample is fractured by static stress. (65:1; 2,600:1)

**420**

**421**

# Effect of chemicals on load fractures

In metallurgy, environmental stress cracking is understood to refer to the simultaneous interaction between a certain sensitive material with a specific medium and tensile stresses. If one of these three components is missing, no stress cracking will occur. This phenomenon is also encountered in polymers.

Apart from stress cracking, permanent changes in mechanical properties can occur due to the inclusion of foreign bodies in the molecule or the removal of certain components. These changes lead to a reduction or an increase in deformability. An example is the partial loosening of the crack tip, leading to accelerated separation. If, in addition, surface crazes occur on the surface under tensile stress, these will enable the attacking medium to penetrate all the more easily into the specimen (see **422**).

Brittle or ductile fractures may occur with one and the same material/attacking medium combination, depending on the amount of tensile stress applied.

**422**

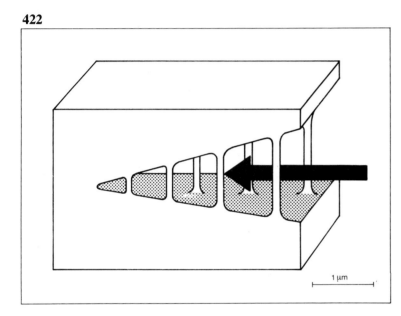

1 μm

**422.** Craze which intersects the surface enables an attacking medium to penetrate inside the material.

## ENVIRONMENTAL STRESS CRACKING

Stress cracking occurs in polymers when the following factors act simultaneously: delicate material, specific attacking medium and tensile stresses. If one of these three is absent, there will be no stress cracking.

The characteristic features of true stress cracking are fracture surfaces with feathery patterns, gaping cracks at right-angles to the main fracture surface and micro-peaks (0.1μm diameter, length 0.3μm).

**423**

**423.** Stress cracking in SAN. An SAN sample was immersed in a mixture of olive oil and oleic acid and subjected to tensile stress. The fracture lies at right angles to the tensile stress and does not show any external constrictions. (21:1)

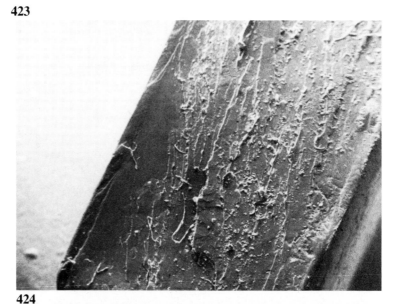

**424**

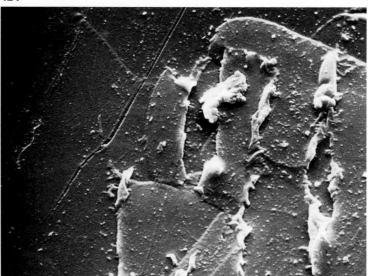

**424, 425.** Stress cracking in SAN. An SAN sample was immersed in a mixture of olive oil and oleic acid and subjected to tensile stress. The fracture surface shows only few indications of residual ductility in the form of isolated, pulled-up films and peaks. Without attacking medium, this material produces ductile force fractures with slight deformation of the fracture surfaces, but pronounced peak structures (see also **308** and **309**). (550:1; 2,200:1)

**425**

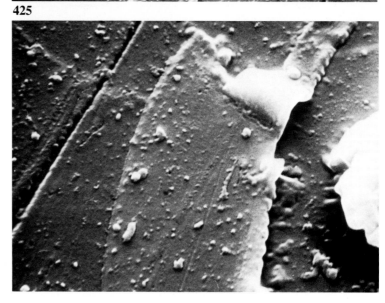

**426–428.** Effect of 60% chromic acid on SAN after 30 minutes. Surface attack and cracking can be observed only near a mechanically produced scratch. The mechanical surface deformation produced internal stresses in the material which led to stress cracking. The spherical structure presumably corresponds to the primary structure. (1,000:1; 10,000:1; 20,000:1)

426

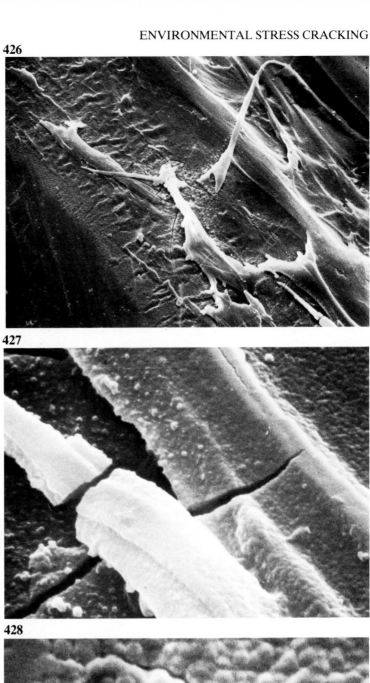

427

428

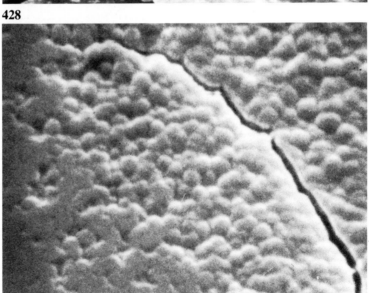

**429, 430.** Stress cracking in glass fibre reinforced PC, caused by carbon tetrachloride. The fracture has a slate-like appearance due to the many cleavage surfaces. Characteristic features are feathery structures, secondary cracks at right angles to the main fracture surface and micro-peaks (diameter $0.2\mu m$) as signs of residual ductility. (1,100:1; 5,500:1)

**429**

**430**

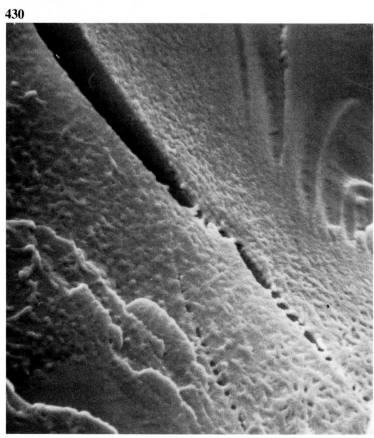

# PERMANENT EMBRITTLEMENT AFTER EXPOSURE TO CHEMICALS

(Fracture following chemical attack)

The presence of chemicals can hinder the mobility of the macromolecules, resulting in reduced deformability. The material is permanently changed and its properties differ considerably from those of the original material. This behaviour is different from the formation of stress cracks, where fracture is caused only by the simultaneous action of tensile stresses and medium. Separation occurs after there has been sufficient embrittlement through externally applied stresses or internal stresses which are increased by the embrittlement.

**431, 432.** A laboratory PP sample became embrittled when immersed in 10% NaOH at 50°C, embrittlement extending to a depth of about $40\mu m$ from the surface. Many parallel, brittle cracks were formed, followed by ductile deformation fractures lower down. (21:1; 500:1)

**431**

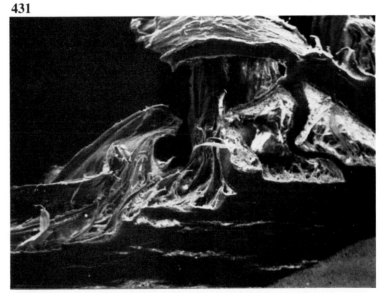

**432**

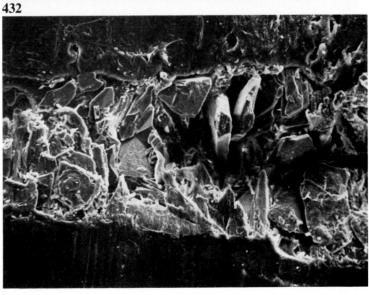

**433, 434.** Level, brittle fracture surfaces (from **432**) without any sign of peaks or lips demonstrate the embrittlement of the surface by Na0H. In between them, ductile residue zones can be distinguished. (2,000:1; 5,000:1)

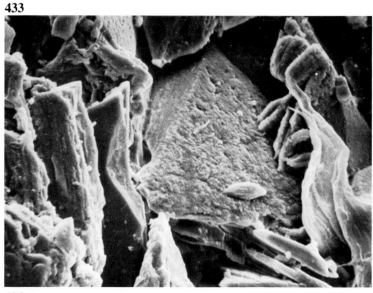

**435.** A nylon 66 laboratory sample failed in the tensile test under reduced tensile stress. Isolated, smooth brittle fracture surfaces can be discerned. It could be that iodine, proved to be present by energy-dispersive micro-analysis, was responsible for the embrittlement. Furthermore, iron and copper were found within the brittle fracture surfaces. (550:1)

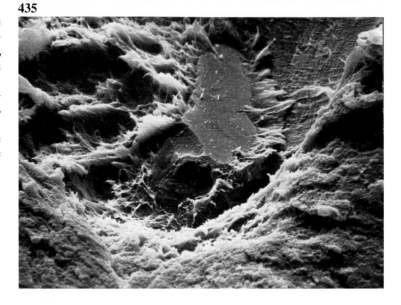

**436–438.** A POM gear wheel which had been exposed to oil vapours failed because of marked shrinkage. Numerous brittle cracks passed through the damaged zone. (See also **198**, **199** and **200**). (2,200:1; 11,000:1; 11,000:1)

**436**

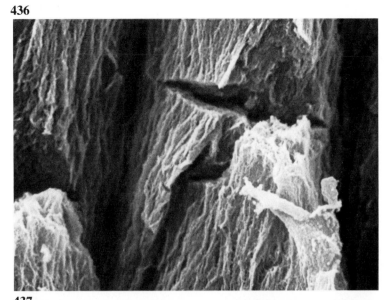

**437**

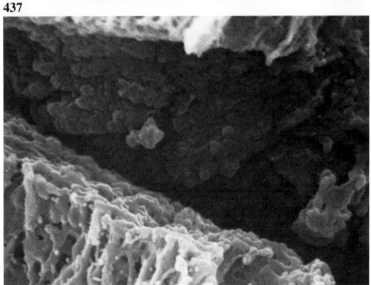

**438**

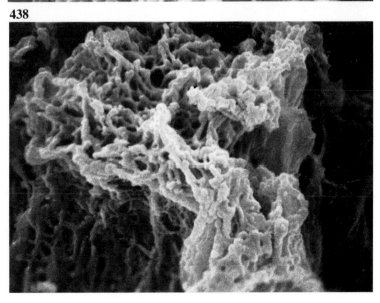

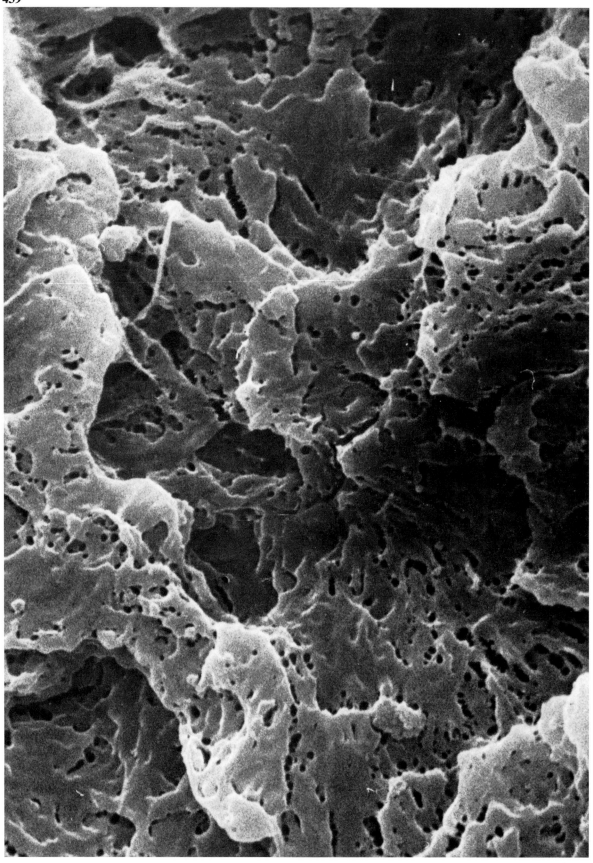

**439, 440.** A POM sample was immersed in water at 23°C (pH=7.5). This caused permanent embrittlement. In the absence of water the material shows a ductile fracture (**288**). (7,000:1; 5,500:1)

**441, 442.** A PP pipe fractured when in contact with alkaline bleaching powder solution (Na0H/Na0C1). The cracks spread from the inside surface of the pipe (bottom left in **442**) and propagated along several fronts throughout the pipe cross-section. At the back right-hand side in **441** lies the ductile laboratory force fracture.

In the brittle fracture surface knots as well as holes up to about 1μm in diameter can be distinguished. These are presumably points along primary polymerisation structures which had separated rather like a snap fastener. (20:1; 5,000:1)

**440**

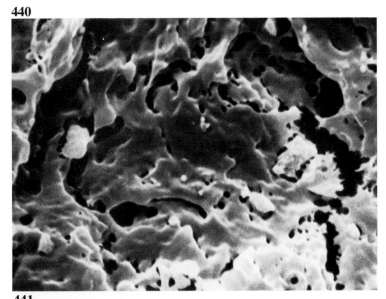

**441**

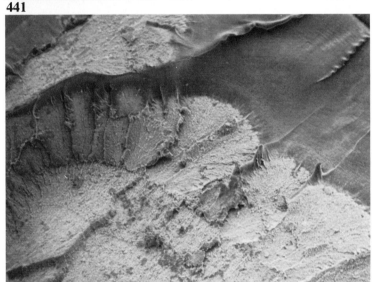

**442**

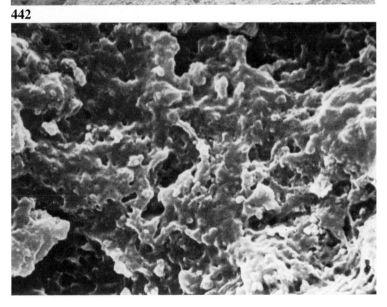

**443, 444.** An HDPE pipe became embrittled by being exposed to sulphuric acid ($H_2SO_4$). Embrittlement began through acid diffusing into the surface, resulting in a network of cracks which became more and more branched. The mechanism of crack formation and the block-like fracture pieces with a feathery structure indicate that embrittlement is permanent and caused by a chemical. It is probable that the basic material had been sulphonated by the acid. (60:1; 1,200:1)

**443**

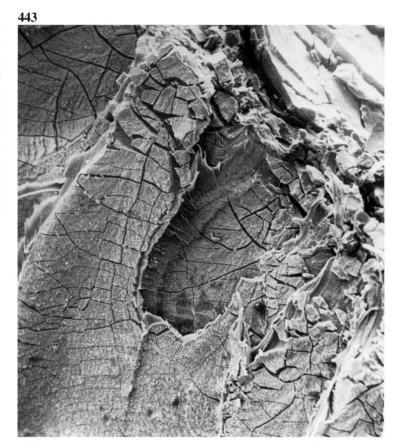

**444**

# INCREASED DUCTILITY CAUSED BY CHEMICAL ATTACK
(Softening effect)

Immersion in chemicals which reduce the intermolecular bonds increases ductility. This occurs, for example, with:

PA in zinc chloride solution or water.

PVC in methanol.

PE in 10% NaOH at 50°C.

PE in 5% Nekanil Extra solution (detergent).

PP in 10% NaOH at 60°C.

**445, 446.** Nylon 6, exposed to zinc chloride solution at 23°C, swelled and absorbed 10% moisture, and failed when subjected to tensile stresses. The sharply defined failure zone is a craze. The material opened up in many places inside and continued to crack in circular fronts until these joined up with adjacent fronts. The water had the effect of reducing the intermolecular bonds (softening effect). (23:1; 110:1)

445

446

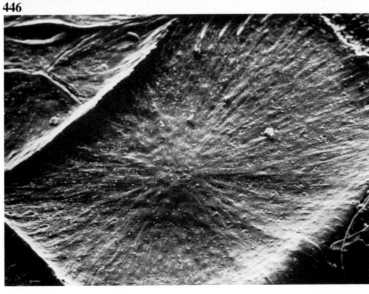

**447, 448.** Crack structures of two surface cracks and end of the craze front, produced at 23°C in zinc chloride (from **455**). The force fracture situated outside the craze (**448**, top) with the short peak structures indicates reduced ductility. (550:1; 2,200:1)

**447**

**448**

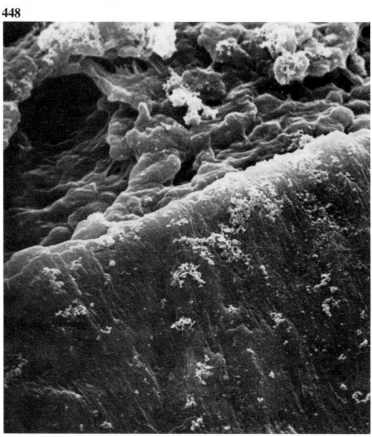

**449, 450.** The effect of 10% NaOH on HDPE resulted in an increase in ductility (very long fibrils) compared with the fracture produced without the attacking agent (see also **281** and **282**). Parallel surface cracks indicate that external influences participated in causing fracture. Here we have an example of the softening effect, i.e. increased ductility through reduction of the intermolecular bonds. (50:1; 500:1)

449

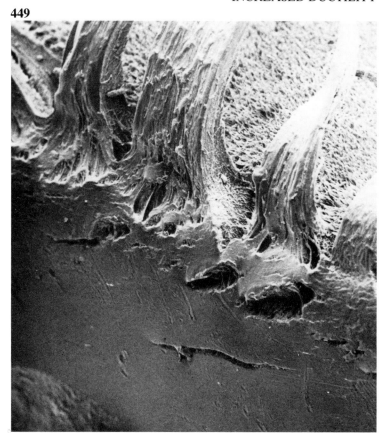

450

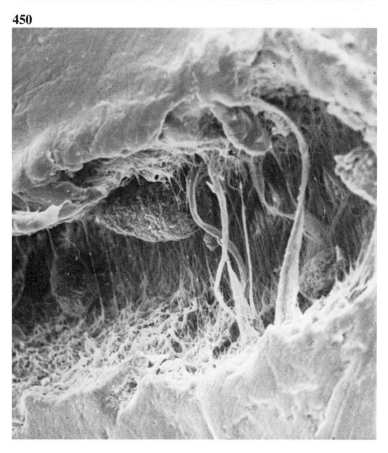

# PARTIAL SOLUTION OF CRACK TIP BY CHEMICALS

This type of damage always occurs when chemicals dissolve the material at the tip of the crack and thereby accelerate crack propagation (**451**).

**451**

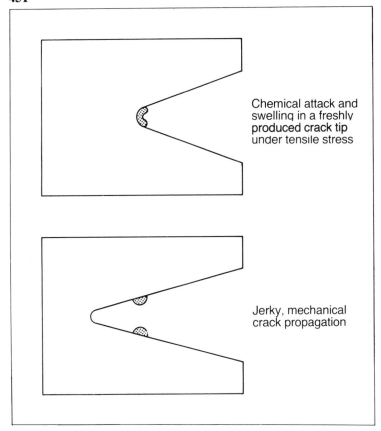

Chemical attack and swelling in a freshly produced crack tip under tensile stress

Jerky, mechanical crack propagation

**451.** Crack propagation in PVC, caused by acetone.

**452.** A sample of PVC sheet, immersed in acetone for 90 minutes, showed several parallel surface cracks. Photograph of the sawn surface prior to immersion in acetone. (24:1)

**453.** A crack in the sample shown in **454**, which had been opened with a knife, showing a roughly semielliptical fracture surface. This means that the crack spread from the sawn surface. The knife cut can be seen at the top of the photograph. (21:1)

**454**

**454–456.** Crack formation in a sample of PVC sheet which had been immersed in acetone for 90 minutes. Along the crack front (top of **454**) the crack has left parallel lines as it progressed. The latest line (the topmost in **454**) represents a flat bead and smooth bands can be distinguished in front of it and behind. The fine bead is the result of chemical attack in the crack tip (swelling), the smooth bands have been formed through spontaneous, jerky crack propagation. The acetone changed the older fracture zones so much, due to swelling, that a plaited pattern was formed after the sample had dried (**455**). No bands can be seen in the oldest fracture zones at the start of the crack. The effect on the fresh fracture surfaces is much greater than on the outer surface of the sheet (cf. **181** and **182**). (1,000:1; 10,000:1; 10,000:1)

**455**

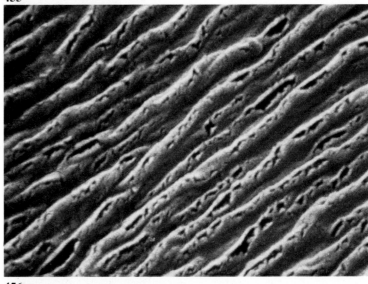

**456**

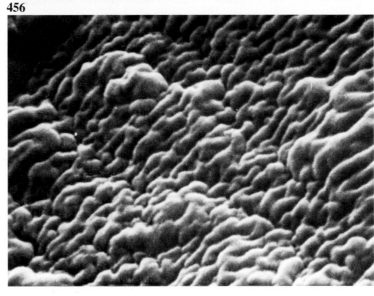

# Appendix

# Abbreviations for polymer names (based on BS 3502 and ISO 1043)

**Homopolymers**

| | |
|---|---|
| CA | Cellulose acetate |
| CAB | Cellulose acetate butyrate |
| CAP | Cellulose acetate propionate |
| CF | Cresol-formaldehyde |
| CMC | Carboxymethylcellulose |
| CN | Cellulose nitrate |
| CP | Cellulose propionate |
| CS | Casein |
| CTA | Cellulose triacetate |
| EC | Ethyl cellulose |
| EP | Epoxide |
| MC | Methyl cellulose |
| MF | Melamine-formaldehyde |
| MPF | Melamine-phenol-formaldehyde |
| PA | Polyamide |
| PAN | Polyacrylonitrile |
| PB | Polybutene-1 |
| PBTP | Polybutyleneterephthalate |
| PC | Polycarbonate |
| PCTFE | Polychlortrifluoroethylene |
| PE | Polyethylene |
| PEOX | Polyethylene oxide |
| PETP | Polyethyleneterephthalate |
| PF | Phenol-formaldehyde |
| PIB | Polyisobutylene |
| PMMA | Polymethyl methacrylate |
| POM | Polyoxymethylene |
| PP | Polypropylene |
| PPO | Polyphenylene oxide |
| PS | Polystyrene |
| PTFE | Polytetrafluoroethylene |
| PUR | Polyurethane |
| PVAC | Polyvinyl acetate |
| PVAL | Polyvinyl alcohol |
| PVB | Polyvinyl butyral |
| PVC | Polyvinyl chloride |
| PVDC | Polyvinylidene chloride |
| PVDF | Polyvinylidene fluoride |
| PVF | Polyvinyl fluoride |
| PVFM | Polyvinyl formal |
| PVK | Polyvinyl carbazole |
| PVP | Polyvinyl pyrrolidone |
| RF | Resorcinol-formaldehyde |
| SI | Silicone |
| UF | Urea-formaldehyde |
| UP | Unsaturated polyester |

**Copolymers and polymer blends**

| | |
|---|---|
| ABS | Acrylonitrile-butadiene-styrene |
| A/MMA | Acrylonitrile-methyl methacrylate |
| A/S/A | Acrylonitrile-styrene-acrylate |
| E/EA | Ethylene-ethyl acrylate |
| E/P | Ethylene-propylene |
| E/VAC | Ethylene-vinyl acetate |
| SAN | Styrene-acrylonitrile |
| SP | Styrene-butadiene |
| SMS | Styrene-αmethyl styrene |
| VC/E | Vinyl chloride-ethylene |
| VC/E/MA | Vinyl chloride-ethylene-methyl acrylate |
| VC/E/VAC | Vinyl chloride-ethylene-vinyl acetate |
| VC/MA | Vinyl chloride-methyl acrylate |
| VC/MMA | Vinyl chloride-methyl methacrylate |
| VC/OA | Vinyl chloride-octyl acrylate |
| VC/VAC | Vinyl chloride-vinyl acetate |
| VC/VDC | Vinyl chloride-vinylidene chloride |

**Reinforced polymers**

| | |
|---|---|
| GRP | Glass fibre reinforced plastics based on thermo-setting resins |
| FRP<br>FRTP | Reinforced thermoplastic materials |

**Rubbers**

| | |
|---|---|
| ABR | Acrylate-butadiene rubbers |
| BR | Butadiene rubbers |
| CR | Chloroprene rubbers |
| IIR | Isobutene-isoprene rubbers |
| IR | Isoprene rubbers (synthetic) |
| NBR | Nitrile-butadiene rubbers |
| NCR | Nitrile-chloroprene rubbers |
| NR | Isoprene rubbers (natural) |
| PBR | Pyridine-butadiene rubbers |
| SBR | Styrene-butadiene rubbers |
| SCR | Styrene-chloroprene rubbers |
| SIR | Styrene-isoprene rubbers |
| NIR | Nitrile-isoprene rubbers |
| PSBR | Pyridine-styrene-butadiene rubbers |
| XSBR | Carboxylic-styrene-butadiene rubbers |
| XNBR | Carboxylic-nitrile-butadiene rubbers |
| BIIR | Bromo-isobutene-isoprene rubbers |
| CIIR | Chloro-isobutene-isoprene rubbers |
| AU | Polyester rubbers |
| EU | Polyether rubbers |

**Miscellaneous**

| | |
|---|---|
| EPDM | Ethylene-propylene terpolymers |
| HDPE | High density polyethylene |
| LDPE | Low density polyethylene |
| PA 6 | ε-caprolactam polymers |
| PA 66 | Homopolycondensate of hexamethylenediamine and adipic acid |
| PA 610 | Homopolycondensate of hexamethylenediamine and sebacic acid |
| PA 11 | Polycondensate of 11-aminoundecanoic acid |
| PA 12 | Homopolymer of laurinlactam |
| PA 66/610 | Copolymer of PA 66 and PA 610 |
| PA 6/12 | Copolymer of PA 6 and PA 12 |

# A simple method of identifying thermoplastic polymers*

The following instructions are based on a few, easily carried out tests which enable thermoplastic polymers to be differentiated according to a few clear characteristics.

## Materials and equipment needed for tests

1. A small container filled with water, for the flotation test;
2. a cigarette lighter for the burning test;
3. some carbon tetrachloride and ethyl acetate for the solvent test;
4. a Bunsen burner or a soldering torch and copper wire for the Beilstein test.

This is all that is needed to narrow down the number of possible polymers, using the table on the next two pages, until the polymer is finally identified.

## Experimental details

The table (pages 246–247) is easy to use. The horizontal column at the top gives the abbreviations of the most common thermoplastics (the explanation of abbreviations is given opposite). The tests are carried out in the following order.

*(a) Flotation test:* this separates the thermoplastics into those that are lighter than water and those that are heavier. A wash basin filled with water, or a glass of water, is usually all that is needed. Samples which are too big, or which contain metal components, can be tested by slicing off a piece which, however, should be placed in water containing a small amount of detergent.

*(b) Burning test:* the sample is ignited with a cigarette lighter or match. It should be noted whether drops of molten plastic are formed.

*(c) Solvent test:* a drop of solvent is applied to the sample and rubbed with the finger to see whether the material is attacked.

*(d) Beilstein test:* a piece of copper wire is held in the flame of a Bunsen burner and the sample then touched with it. The wire is then returned to the Bunsen flame. If a halogen was present, the flame will be tinged a definite green.

When these tests have been carried out one will often be able to see what thermoplastic is present. If it still cannot be definitely identified, this can then be done by the fingernail test, the smell test or the fracture test.

These tests can, however, be used to identify thermoplastic groups only, e.g. polyamides, polyethylenes etc. If you want to subdivide further within a particular group, more extensive tests are necessary. If, for example, you want to find out which type of polyamide is present, the material's melting point or its solubility in formic acid must be determined. Often, however, it is sufficient to be able to identify the type of thermoplastic and this can be quickly, easily and reliably done with this technique.

*From N. N. Werkstoffblatt 110. 1, BASF, Ludwigschafen, 1973.

**Explanation of abbreviations used in the table overleaf**

| | |
|---|---|
| PMP | poly-4-methylpentene-1 |
| PE | polyethylene |
| PP | polypropylene |
| SB+T | high impact polystyrene + blowing agent |
| ABS+T | acrylonitrile-butadiene-styrene + blowing agent |
| PE+F | polyethylene + flame retardant |
| PP+F | polypropylene + flame retardant |
| CAB | cellulose acetate butyrate |
| PA | polyamide |
| POM | polyformaldehyde |
| PMMA | polymethyl methacrylate |
| PBT | polybutylene terephthalate |
| CA | cellulose acetate |
| PS | polystyrene |
| SB | styrene-butadiene, high impact polystyrene |
| SAN | styrene-acrylonitrile copolymer |
| ABS | acrylonitrile-butadiene-styrene copolymer |
| PVC-W | plasticised polyvinyl chloride |
| PSO | polysulphone |
| PC | polycarbonate |
| PPO-M | modified polyphenylene oxide |
| SB+F | high impact polystyrene + flame retardant |
| ABS+F | acrylonitrile-butadiene-styrene + flame retardant |
| PVC-H | unplasticised PVC |
| PA+F | polyamide + flame retardant |

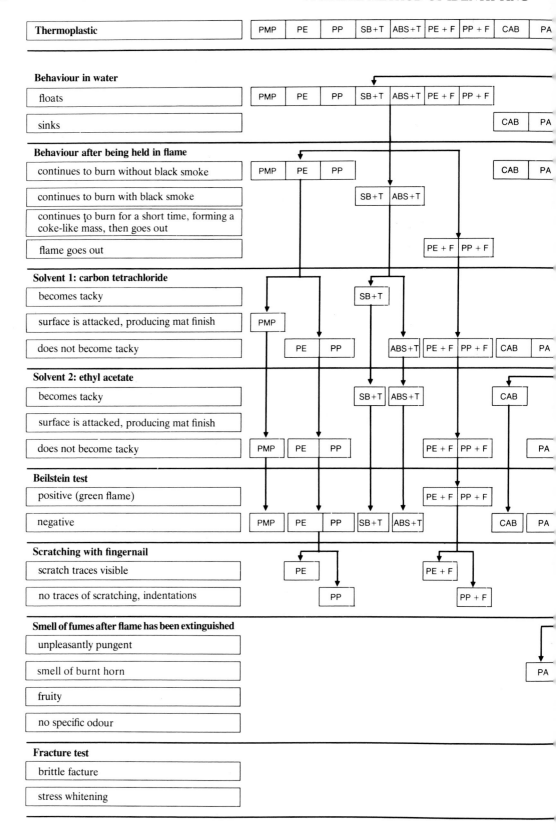

| Thermoplastic | PMP | PE | PP | SB+T | ABS+T | PE + F | PP + F | CAB | PA |
|---|---|---|---|---|---|---|---|---|---|

**Behaviour in water**
- floats
- sinks

**Behaviour after being held in flame**
- continues to burn without black smoke
- continues to burn with black smoke
- continues to burn for a short time, forming a coke-like mass, then goes out
- flame goes out

**Solvent 1: carbon tetrachloride**
- becomes tacky
- surface is attacked, producing mat finish
- does not become tacky

**Solvent 2: ethyl acetate**
- becomes tacky
- surface is attacked, producing mat finish
- does not become tacky

**Beilstein test**
- positive (green flame)
- negative

**Scratching with fingernail**
- scratch traces visible
- no traces of scratching, indentations

**Smell of fumes after flame has been extinguished**
- unpleasantly pungent
- smell of burnt horn
- fruity
- no specific odour

**Fracture test**
- brittle facture
- stress whitening

*can be differentiated by melting point

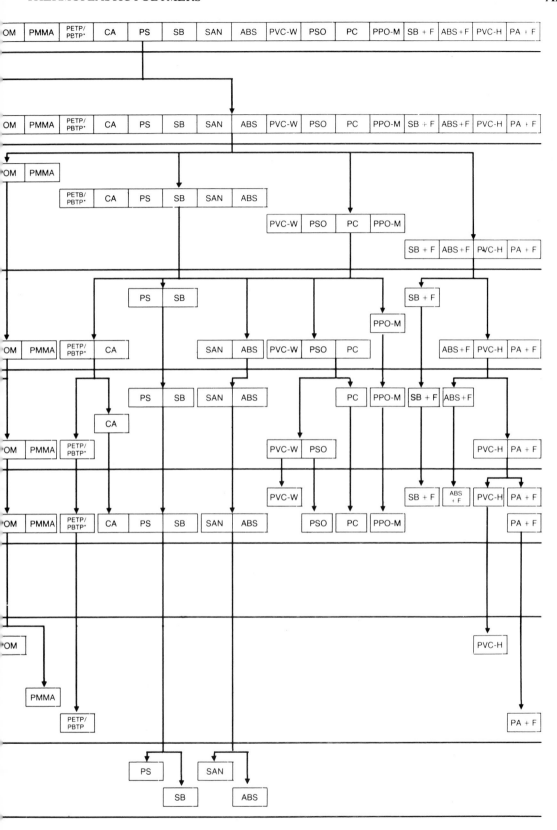

## A guide chart of the approximate physical properties of polymers
(from Domininghaus, H. Die Kunststoffe und ihre Eigenschaften, VDI-Verlag, Düsseldorf, 1976)

| Polymer | Abbreviation | Density (g/cm³) | Tensile strength (N/cm²) | Elongation at break (%) | Modulus of elasticity in tension (N/mm²) | Ball indentation hardness, 10 sec (N/mm²) | Impact strength (Nmm/mm²) | Notched impact strength DIN 53453 Nmm/mm² | Notched impact strength ASTM D 256 ft.-lb inch o.n. | Volume resistivity (Ω cm) | Surface resistance (Ω) | Dielectric constant 50 Hz | Dielectric constant $10^6$ Hz |
|---|---|---|---|---|---|---|---|---|---|---|---|---|---|
| Low density polyethylene | LDPE | 0,914/0,928 | 8/23 | 300/1000 | 200/500 | 13/20 | o. Br. | o. Br. | – | $>10^{17}$ | $10^{14}$ | 2,29 | 2,28 |
| High density polyethylene | HDPE | 0,94/0,96 | 18/35 | 100/1000 | 700/1400 | 40/65 | o. Br. | o. Br. | – | $>10^{17}$ | $10^{14}$ | 2,35 | 2,34 |
| Ethylene/vinyl acetate | EVA | 0,92/0,95 | 10/20 | 600/900 | 7/120 | – | o. Br. | o. Br. | o. Br. | $>10^{15}$ | $10^{13}$ | 2,5/3,2 | 2,6/3,2 |
| Polypropylene | PP | 0,90/0,907 | 21/37 | 20/800 | 1100/1300 | 36/70 | o. Br. | 3/17 | 0,5/20 | $>10^{17}$ | $10^{13}$ | 2,27 | 2,25 |
| Polybutene-1 | – | 0,905/0,920 | 30/38 | 250/280 | 250/350 | 30/38 | o. Br. | 4/o. Br. | o. Br. | $>10^{17}$ | $10^{13}$ | 2,5 | 2,2 |
| Polyisobutylene | PIB | 0,91/0,93 | 2/6 | >1000 | | | o. Br. | o. Br. | o. Br. | $>10^{15}$ | $10^{13}$ | 2,3 | – |
| Poly-4-methylpentene-1 | – | 0,83 | 25/28 | 13/22 | 1100/1500 | – | – | – | 0,4/0,6 | $>10^{16}$ | $10^{13}$ | 2,12 | 2,12 |
| Ionomers | – | 0,94/0,96 | 28/35 | 250/4501 | 180/210 | – | – | – | 6/15 | $>10^{16}$ | $10^{13}$ | | |
| Unplasticised polyvinyl chloride | uPVC | 1,38/1,55 | 50/75 | 10/50 | 1000/3500 | 75/155 | o. Br./>20 | 2/50 | 0,4/20 | $>10^{15}$ | $10^{13}$ | 3,5 | 3,0 |
| Plasticised polyvinyl chloride | – | 1,16/1,35 | 10/25 | 170/400 | – | – | o. Br. | o. Br. | – | $>10^{11}$ | $10^{11}$ | 4/8 | 4/4,5 |
| Polystyrene | PS | 1,05 | 45/65 | 3/4 | 3200/3250 | 120/130 | 5/20 | 2/2,5 | 0,25/0,6 | $>10^{16}$ | $>10^{13}$ | 2,5 | 2,5 |
| Styrene/acrylonitrile copolymer | SAN | 1,08 | 75 | 5 | 3600 | 130/140 | 8/20 | 2/3 | 0,35/0,5 | $>10^{16}$ | $>10^{13}$ | 2,6/3,4 | 2,6/3,1 |
| Styrene/polybutadiene graft polymer | SB | 1,05 | 26/38 | 25/60 | 1800/2500 | 80/130 | 10/80 | 5/13 | – | $>10^{16}$ | $>10^{13}$ | 2,4/4 7 | 2,4/3,8 |
| Acrylonitrile/polybutadiene/styrene graft polymer | ABS | 1,04/1,06 | 32/45 | 15/30 | 1900/2700 | 80/120 | 70/o. Br. | 7/20 | 2,5/12 | $>10^{15}$ | $>10^{13}$ | 2,4/5 | 2,4/3,8 |
| AN/AN elastomer/styrene graft polymer | ASA | 1,04 | 32 | 40 | 1800 | 75 | | 18 | 6/8 | $>10^{15}$ | $>10^{13}$ | 3/4 | 3/3,5 |
| Polymethyl methacrylate | PMMA | 1,17/1,20 | 50/77 | 2/10 | 2700/3200 | 180/200 | 18 | 2 | 0,3/0,5 | $>10^{15}$ | $10^{15}$ | 3,3/3,9 | 2,2/3,2 |
| Polyvinyl carbazol | – | 1,19 | 20/30 | – | 3500 | 200 | 5 | 2 | – | $>10^{16}$ | $10^{14}$ | – | 3 |
| Polyacetal | POM | 1,41/1,42 | 62/70 | 25/70 | 2800/3200 | 150/170 | 100 | 8 | 1/2,3 | $>10^{15}$ | $10^{13}$ | 3,7 | 3,7 |
| Polytetrafluoroethylene | PTFE | 2,15/2,20 | 25/36 | 350/550 | 410 | 27/35 | o. Br. | 13/15 | 3,0 | $>10^{18}$ | $10^{17}$ | <2,1 | <2,1 |
| Tetrafluoroethylene/hexafluoropropylene copolymer | PFEP | 2,12/2,17 | 22/28 | 250/330 | 350 | 30/32 | – | | o. Br. | $>10^{18}$ | $10^{17}$ | 2,1 | 2,1 |
| Polytrifluorochloroethylene | PCTFE | 2,10/2,12 | 32/40 | 120/175 | 1050/2100 | 65/70 | o. Br. | 8/10 | 2,5/2,8 | $>10^{18}$ | $10^{16}$ | 2,3/2,8 | 2,3/2,5 |
| Ethylene/tetrafluoroethylene | PETFE | 1,7 | 35/54 | 400/500 | 1100 | 65 | – | | o. Br. | $>10^{16}$ | $10^{13}$ | 2,6 | 2,6 |
| Polyamide 6 | PA 6 | 1,13 | 70/85 | 200/300 | 1400 | 75 | o. Br. | o. Br. | 3,0 | $10^{12}$ | $10^{10}$ | 3,8 | 3,4 |
| Polyamide 66 | PA 66 | 1,14 | 77/84 | 150/300 | 2000 | 100 | o. Br. | 15/20 | 2,1 | $10^{12}$ | $10^{10}$ | 8,0 | 4,0 |
| Polyamide 11 | PA 11 | 1,04 | 56 | 500 | 1000 | 75 | o. Br. | 30/40 | 1,8 | $10^{13}$ | $10^{11}$ | 3,7 | 3,5 |
| Polyamide 12 | PA 12 | 1,02 | 56/65 | 300 | 1600 | 75 | o. Br. | 10/20 | 2/5,5 | $10^{13}$ | $10^{11}$ | 4,2 | 3,1 |
| Aromatic polyamide | – | 1,12 | 70/84 | 70/150 | 2000 | 160 | o. Br. | 13 | – | $10^{11}$ | $10^{10}$ | 4,0 | 3,0 |
| Polycarbonate | PC | 1,2 | 56/67 | 100/130 | 2100/2400 | 110 | o. Br. | 20/30 | 12/18 | $>10^{17}$ | $>10^{15}$ | 3,0 | 2,9 |
| Polyethyleneterephthalate | PETP | 1,37 | 47 | 50/300 | 3100 | 200 | o. Br. | 4 | 0,8/1,0 | $10^{16}$ | $10^{16}$ | 4,0 | 4,0 |
| Polybutyleneterephthalate | PBTP | 1,31 | 40 | 15 | 2000 | 180 | o. Br. | 4 | 0,8/1,0 | $10^{16}$ | $10^{13}$ | 3,0 | 3,0 |
| Polyphenylene oxide, modified | PPO | 1,06 | 55/68 | 50/60 | 2500 | – | o. Br. | – | 4 | $10^{16}$ | $10^{14}$ | 2,6 | 2,6 |
| Polysulphone | PSU | 1,24 | 50/100 | 25/30 | 2600/2750 | – | – | – | 1,3 | $>10^{16}$ | – | 3,1 | 3,0 |
| Polyphenylene sulphide | PPS | 1,34 | 75 | 3 | 3400 | – | – | – | 0,3 | $>10^{16}$ | – | 3,1 | 3,2 |
| Polyaryl sulphone | PAS | 1,36 | 90 | 13 | 2600 | – | – | – | 1/2 | $>10^{16}$ | – | 3,9 | 3,7 |
| Polyether sulphone | PES | 1,37 | 85 | 30/80 | 2450 | – | – | – | 1,6 | $10^{17}$ | – | 3,5 | 3,5 |
| Polyaryl ether | PAE | 1,14 | 53 | 25/90 | 2250 | – | – | – | 8,0 | $>10^{10}$ | – | 3,14 | 3,10 |
| Phenol-formaldehyde | PF | 1,4 | 25 | 0,4/0,8 | 5600/12000 | 250/320 | >6 | >1,5 | 0,2/0,6 | $10^{11}$ | $>10^{8}$ | 6 | 4,5 |
| Urea-formaldehyde | UF | 1,5 | 30 | 0,5/1,0 | 7000/10500 | 260/350 | >6,5 | >1,5 | 0,5/0,4 | $10^{11}$ | $>10^{10}$ | 8 | 7 |
| Melamine-formaldehyde | MF | 1,5 | 30 | 0,6/0,9 | 4900/9100 | 260/410 | >7,0 | >1,5 | 0,2/0,3 | $10^{11}$ | $>10^{8}$ | 9 | 8 |
| Unsaturated polyester, resin | UP | 2,0 | 30 | 0,6/1,2 | 14000/20000 | 240 | >4,5 | >3,0 | 0,5/16 | $>10^{12}$ | $>10^{10}$ | 6 | 5 |
| Polydiallyl phthalate | PDAP | 1,51/1,78 | 40/75 | – | 9800/15500 | – | – | – | 0,4/15 | $10^{13}/10^{16}$ | $10^{13}$ | 5,2 | 4 |
| Silicone resin | SI | 1,8/1,9 | 28/46 | – | 6000/12000 | – | – | – | 0,3/0,8 | $10^{14}$ | $10^{12}$ | 4 | 3,5 |
| Polyimide | PI | 1,43 | 75/100 | 4/9 | 23000/28000 | – | – | – | 0,5/1,0 | $>10^{16}$ | $>10^{15}$ | 3,5 | 3,4 |
| Epoxy resin | EP | 1,9 | 30/40 | 4 | 21500 | – | >8 | >3 | 2/30 | $>10^{14}$ | $>10^{12}$ | 3,5/5 | 3,5/5 |
| Polyurethane casting resin | PUR | 1,05 | 70/80 | 3/6 | 4000 | – | – | – | 0,4 | $10^{16}$ | $10^{14}$ | 3,6 | 3,4 |
| Thermoplastic PU elastomer | PUR | 1,20 | 30/40 | 400/450 | 700 | – | o. Br. | o. Br. | o. Br. | $10^{12}$ | $10^{11}$ | 6,5 | 5,6 |
| Linear polyurethane (Uso) | PUR | 1,21 | 30 (Ós) | 35 (Eg) | 1000 | – | o. Br. | 3 | – | $10^{13}$ | $10^{12}$ | 5,8 | 4,0 |
| Chlorinated polyether | – | 1,4 | 42 | 130 | 1050 | – | 140 | 100 | 0,4 | $10^{16}$ | $10^{14}$ | 2,8 | 2,5 |
| Vulcanised fibre | – | 1,1/1,45 | 85/100 | – | | 80/140 | 20/120 | | | $10^{10}$ | $10^{8}$ | | |
| Cellulose acetate | CA | 1,30 | 38/(Ós) | 3 (Eg) | 2200 | 50 | 65 | 15 | 2,5 | $10^{13}$ | $10^{12}$ | 5,8 | 4,6 |
| Cellulose propionate | CP | 1,19/1,23 | 14/55 | 30/100 | 420/1500 | 47/79 | o. Br. | 6/20 | 1,5 | $10^{16}$ | $10^{14}$ | 4,2 | 3,7 |
| Cellulose acetate butyrate | CAB | 1,18 | 26 (Ós) | 4 (Eg) | 1600 | 35/43 | o. Br. | 30/35 | 4/5 | $10^{16}$ | $10^{14}$ | 3,7 | 3,5 |

| Electrical | | | | | | | Thermal | | | | | | | | Optical | | Water absorption | |
|---|---|---|---|---|---|---|---|---|---|---|---|---|---|---|---|---|---|---|
| Dissipation factor tan $\delta$ | | Dielectric strength | | Tracking resistance (stage) | | | Maximum service temperature (°C) | | | Heat distortion temperature (°C) | | Coefficient of linear thermal expansion ($K^{-1} \times 10^6$) | Thermal conductivity (W/mK) | Specific heat (KJ/kgK) | Refractive index | Clarity – transl. = translucent, transp. = transparent | | |
| 50 Hz | $10^6$ Hz | kV/25 μm ASTM D 149 | kV/cm DIN 53481 | KA | KB | KC | max. short-term | max. continuous | min. continuous | VSP (Vicat 5 kg) DIN 53460 | ASTM D 648 1,86/945 N/mm² | | | | | | mg (4 d) DIN 53492 | % (24 h) ASTM D 570 |
| $1,5\times10^4$ | $0,8\times10^{-4}$ | >700 | – | 3 b | >600 | >600 | 80/90 | 60/75 | –50 | – | 35 | 250 | 0,32/0,40 | 2,1/2,5 | 1,51 | near transp. | <0,01 | <0,01 |
| $2,4\times10^{-4}$ | $2,0\times10^{-4}$ | >700 | – | 3 c | >600 | >600 | 90/120 | 70/80 | –50 | 60/70 | 50 | 200 | 0,38/0,51 | 2,1/2,7 | 1,53 | near opaque | <0,01 | <0,01 |
| 0,003/0,02 | 0,03/0,05 | – | 620/780 | – | – | – | 65 | 55 | –60 | – | 34/62 | 160/200 | 0,35 | 2,3 | – | transp./opaque | – | 0,05/0,13 |
| $<4\times10^{-4}$ | $<5\times10^{-4}$ | 800 | 500/650 | 3 c | >600 | >600 | 140 | 100 | 0/–30 | 85/100 | 45/120 | 150 | 0,17/0,22 | 2,0 | 1,49 | transp./opaque | <0,01 | 0,01/0,03 |
| $7\times10^{-4}$ | $6\times10^{-4}$ | 700 | * | 3 c | >600 | >600 | 130 | 90 | 0 | 70 | 60/110 | 150 | 0,20 | 1,8 | – | near opaque | <0,01 | <0,02 |
| 0,0004 | – | 230 | – | 3 c | >600 | >600 | 80 | 65 | –50 | – | – | 120 | 0,12/0,20 | – | – | near opaque | <0,01 | <0,01 |
| $7\times10^{-5}$ | $3\times10^{-5}$ | 280 | 700 | 3 c | >600 | >600 | 180 | 120 | 0 | – | – | 117 | 0,17 | 2,18 | 1,46 | near transp. | – | 0,01 |
| | | | | | | | 120 | 100 | –100 | – | 38/45 | 120 | 0,25 | 2,20 | 1,51 | transp. | – | 0,1/1 4 |
| 0,011 | 0,015 | 200/400 | 350/500 | 2/3 b | 600 | 600 | 75/100 | 65/85 | –5 | 75/110 | 60/82 | 70/80 | 0,14/0,17 | 0,85/0,9 | 1,52/1,55 | transp./opaque | 3/18 | 0,04/0,4 |
| 0,08 | 0,12 | 150/300 | 300/400 | – | – | – | 55/65 | 50/55 | 0/–20 | 40 | – | 150/210 | 0,15 | 0,9/1,8 | – | transp./opaque | 6/30 | 0,15/0,75 |
| $1/4\times10^{-4}$ | $0,5/4\times10^{-4}$ | 500 | 300/700 | 1/2 | 140 | 150/25 | 60/80 | 50/70 | –10 | 78/99 | 110/80 | 70 | 0,18 | 1,3 | 1,59 | transp. | – | 0,03/0,1 |
| $6/8\times10^{-3}$ | $7/10\times10^{-3}$ | 500 | 400/500 | 1/2 | 160 | 150/26 | 95 | 85 | –20 | – | 104/90 | 80 | 0,18 | 1,3 | 1,57 | transp. | – | 0,2/0,3 |
| $4/20\times10^{-4}$ | $4/20\times10^{-4}$ | 500 | 300/600 | 2 | >600 | >600 | 60/80 | 50/70 | –20 | 77/95 | 104/82 | 70 | 0,18 | 1,3 | – | opaque | – | 0,05/0,6 |
| $3/8\times10^{-3}$ | $2/15\times10^{-3}$ | 400 | 350/500 | 3 a | >600 | >600 | 85/100 | 75/85 | –40 | 95/110 | 80/120 | 60/110 | 0,18 | 1,3 | – | opaque | – | 0,2/0,45 |
| 0,02/0,05 | 0,02/0,03 | 350 | 360/400 | 3 a | >600 | >600 | 85/90 | 70/75 | –40 | 92 | 100/110 | 80/110 | 0,18 | 1,3 | – | transp./opaque | – | |
| 0,04/0,06 | 0,004/0,04 | 300 | 400/500 | 3 c | >600 | >600 | 85/100 | 65/90 | –40 | 70/100 | 60/100 | 70 | 0,18 | 1,47 | 1,49 | transp. | 35/45 | 0,1/0,4 |
| $6/10\times10^{-4}$ | $6/10\times10^{-4}$ | 500 | – | 3 b | >600 | >600 | 170 | 160 | –100 | 180 | – | – | 0,29 | – | – | opaque | 0,5 | 0,1/0,2 |
| 0,005 | 0,005 | 700 | 380/500 | 3 b | >600 | >600 | 110/140 | 90/110 | –60 | 160/173 | 110/170 | 90/110 | 0,25/0,30 | – | 1,46 | opaque | 20/30 | 0,22/0,25 |
| $<2\times10^{-4}$ | $<2\times10^{-4}$ | 500 | 480 | 3 c | >600 | >600 | 300 | 250 | –200 | – | –/121 | 100 | 0,25 | 1,0 | 1,35 | opaque | – | 0 |
| $<2\times10^{-4}$ | $<7\times10^{-4}$ | 500 | 550 | 3 c | >600 | >600 | 250 | 205 | –100 | – | –/70 | 80 | 0,25 | 1,12 | 1,34 | transp./transl. | – | <0,1 |
| $1\times10^{-3}$ | $2\times10^{-2}$ | 500 | 550 | 3 c | >600 | >600 | 180 | 150 | –40 | – | –/126 | 60 | 0,22 | 0,9 | 1,43 | transl./opaque | – | 0 |
| $8\times10^{-3}$ | $5\times10^{-3}$ | 380 | 400 | 3 c | >600 | >600 | 220 | 150 | –190 | – | 71/104 | 40 | 0,23 | 0,9 | 1,40 | transl./opaque | – | 0,03 |
| 0,01 | 0,03 | 350 | 400 | 3 b | >600 | >600 | 140/180 | 80/100 | –30 | 180 | 80/190 | 80 | 0,29 | 1,7 | 1,53 | transl./opaque | – | 1,3/1,9 |
| 0,14 | 0,08 | 400 | 600 | 3 b | >600 | >600 | 170/200 | 80/120 | –30 | 200 | 105/200 | 80 | 0,23 | 1,7 | 1,53 | transl./opaque | – | 1,5 |
| 0,06 | 0,04 | 300 | 425 | 3 b | >600 | >600 | 140/150 | 70/80 | –70 | 175 | 150/130 | 130 | 0,23 | 1,26 | 1,52 | transl./opaque | – | 0,3 |
| 0,04 | 0,03 | 300 | 450 | 3 b | >600 | >600 | 140/150 | 70/80 | –70 | 165 | 140/150 | 150 | 0,23 | 1,26 | – | transl./opaque | – | 0,25 |
| 0,03 | 0,04 | 250 | 350 | 3 b | >600 | >600 | 130/140 | 80/100 | –70 | 145 | 140/80 | 80 | 0,23 | 1,6 | 1,53 | transp. | – | 0,4 |
| $7\times10^{-4}$ | $1\times10^{-2}$ | 350 | 380 | 1 | 120/160 | 260/30 | 160 | 135 | –100 | 138 | 130/145 | 60/70 | 0,21 | 1,17 | 1,58 | transp. | 10 | 0,16 |
| $2\times10^{-3}$ | $2\times10^{-2}$ | 500 | 420 | 2 | – | – | 200 | 100 | –20 | 188 | – | 70 | 0,24 | 1,05 | – | transp./opaque | 18/20 | 0,30 |
| $2\times10^{-3}$ | $2\times10^{-2}$ | 500 | 420 | 3 b | 420 | 380 | 165 | 100 | –30 | 178 | 50/190 | 60 | 0,21 | 1,30 | – | opaque | – | 0,08 |
| $4\times10^{-4}$ | $9\times10^{-4}$ | 500 | 450 | 1 | 300 | 300 | 150 | 80 | –30 | 148 | 100/140 | 60 | 0,23 | 1,40 | – | opaque | – | 0,06 |
| $8\times10^{-4}$ | $3\times10^{-3}$ | – | 425 | 1 | 175 | 175 | 200 | 150 | –100 | – | 175/180 | 54 | 0,28 | 1,30 | 1,63 | transp./opaque | – | 0,02 |
| $4\times10^{-4}$ | $7\times10^{-4}$ | – | 595 | – | – | – | 300 | 200 | – | – | 137/– | 55 | 0,25 | – | – | opaque | – | 0,02 |
| $3\times10^{-3}$ | $13\times10^{-3}$ | – | 350 | – | – | – | 300 | 260 | – | – | – | 47 | 0,16 | – | 1,67 | opaque | – | 1,8 |
| $1\times10^{-3}$ | $6\times10^{-3}$ | – | 400 | – | – | – | 260 | 200 | – | – | – | 55 | 0,18 | 1,10 | 1,65 | transp. | – | 0,43 |
| $6\times10^{-3}$ | $7\times10^{-3}$ | – | 430 | – | – | – | 160 | 120 | – | – | 150/160 | 65 | 0,26 | 1,46 | – | transl./opaque | – | 0,25 |
| 0,1 | 0,03 | 50/100 | 300/400 | 1 | 140/180 | 125/17 | 140 | 110 | – | – | 150/190 | 30/50 | 0,35 | 1,30 | – | opaque | <150 | 0,3/1,2 |
| 0,04 | 0,3 | 80/150 | 300/400 | 3 a | >400 | >600 | 100 | 70 | – | – | 130/– | 50/60 | 0,40 | 1,20 | – | opaque | <300 | 0,4/0,8 |
| 0,06 | 0,03 | 80/150 | 290/300 | 3 b | >500 | >600 | 120 | 80 | – | – | 180/– | 50/60 | 0,50 | 1,20 | – | opaque | <250 | 0,1/0,6 |
| 0,04 | 0,02 | 120 | 250/530 | 3 c | >600 | >600 | 200 | 150 | – | – | 230/– | 20/40 | 0,70 | 1,20 | – | opaque | <45 | 0,03/0,5 |
| 0,04 | 0,03 | – | 400 | 3 c | >600 | >600 | 190/250 | 150/180 | –50 | – | 220/– | 10/35 | 0,60 | – | – | opaque | – | 0,12/0,35 |
| 0,03 | 0,02 | – | 200/400 | 3 c | >600 | >600 | 250 | 170/180 | –50 | – | 480/– | 20/50 | 0,3/0,4 | 0,8/0,9 | – | opaque | – | 0,2 |
| $2\times10^{-3}$ | $5\times10^{-3}$ | – | 560 | 1 | >300 | >380 | 400 | 260 | –200 | – | 240/– | 50/63 | 0,6/0,65 | – | – | opaque | – | 0.32 |
| 0,001 | 0,01 | – | 300/400 | 3 c | >300 | 200/60 | 180 | 130 | – | – | 200/– | 11/35 | 0,88 | 0,8 | – | opaque | <30 | 0,05/0,2 |
| 0,05 | 0,05 | – | 240 | 3 c | – | – | 100 | 80 | – | – | 90/– | 10/20 | 0,58 | 1,76 | – | transp. | – | 0,1/0,2 |
| 0,03 | 0,06 | – | 300/600 | 3 a | >600 | >600 | 110 | 80 | –40 | – | – | 150 | 1,7 | 0,5 | – | transl./opaque | – | 0,7/0,9 |
| 0,12 | 0,07 | 330 | – | – | – | – | 80 | 60 | –15 | 100 | – | 210 | 1,8 | 0,4 | – | transl./opaque | 130 | – |
| 0,01 | 0,01 | 400 | 400 | – | – | – | 150 | 120 | –60 | – | 99/140 | 150 | 0,15 | – | – | opaque | – | 0,9 |
| 0,08 | – | 70/180 | – | – | – | – | 180 | 105 | –30 | – | – | – | – | – | – | opaque | – | 7/9 |
| 0,02 | 0,03 | 320 | 400 | 3 a | >600 | >600 | 80 | 70 | –40 | 50/63 | 90/– | 120 | 0,22 | 1,6 | 1,50 | transp. | 130 | 6 |
| 0,01 | 0,03 | 350 | 400 | 3 a | >600 | >600 | 80/120 | 60/115 | –40 | 100 | 73/98 | 110/130 | 0,21 | 1,7 | 1,47 | transp. | 40/60 | 1,2/2,8 |
| 0,006 | 0,021 | 380 | 400 | 3 a | >600 | >600 | 80/120 | 60/115 | –40 | 60/75 | 62/71 | 120 | 0,21 | 1,6 | 1,47 | transp. | 40/60 | 0,9/3,2 |

# APPENDIX

## The chemical resistance of important polymers

(from Oberbach, K. Kunststoff-Kennwerte für Konstrukteure, Carl Hanser Verlag, München, 1975)

+ resistant
⊕ resistant to moderately resistant
○ moderately resistant
⊖ moderately resistant to not resistant
− not resistant

| Polymer | | Water | Acids | | Hydrofluoric acid | Alkalis | | Inorganic salts | Halogens | Oxidising agents | Solvents | | | | | | | | | | | | |
| --- | --- | --- | --- | --- | --- | --- | --- | --- | --- | --- | --- | --- | --- | --- | --- | --- | --- | --- | --- | --- | --- | --- | --- |
| | | | Dilute | Concentrated | | Dilute | Concentrated | | | | Aliphatic hydrocarbons | Halogen alkanes | Alcohols | Ethers | Esters | Ketones | Aldehydes | Amines | Organic acids | Aromatic compounds | Fuels | Petroleum | Fats, oils |
| Low density polyethylene | LDPE | + | + | + | + | + | + | + | − | − | ⊖ | − | ○ | − | ○ | ○ | | | + | − | ⊖ | ○ | ⊕ |
| Medium density polyethylene | MDPE | + | + | + | + | + | + | + | − | − | ⊖ | − | + | ○ | ⊕ | ⊕ | ⊕ | + | + | ⊕ | ⊕ | ⊕ | ⊕ |
| High density polyethylene | HDPE | + | + | + | + | + | + | + | − | − | ⊖ | + | ○ | + | + | | | | + | ⊕ | ⊕ | ⊕ | + |
| Polyethylene, sulphochl | — | | + | + | + | + | + | + | ○ | ○ | ⊕ | ⊖ | + | ○ | − | ○ | ⊖ | + | ⊕ | ⊖ | ○ | ⊕ | ○ |
| Ethylene-vinyl acetate | EVA | | + | ⊖ | | + | + | + | − | ⊖ | ⊖ | − | ⊕ | ⊖ | ⊖ | − | + | ⊕ | ⊕ | | ○ | ○ | ⊕ |
| Polyisobutylene | PIB | + | + | + | + | + | + | + | ○ | ○ | − | − | + | − | − | ⊕ | ⊖ | + | + | − | − | − | − |
| Polyisobutylene, filled | PIB | + | + | + | + | ○ | + | + | | ○ | − | − | + | − | − | ⊖ | ⊖ | + | ⊕ | ⊖ | ⊖ | ○ | − |
| Polypropylene | PP | + | + | ⊕ | ⊕ | + | + | + | ⊖ | − | ⊕ | ⊖ | + | ○ | ⊕ | ⊕ | + | + | ⊕ | ⊖ | ⊕ | + | + |
| Polymethylpentene | PMP | + | + | + | | + | + | + | − | ⊖ | − | ⊖ | ⊕ | − | ⊖ | ○ | + | | ⊕ | ⊖ | ○ | ⊕ | + |
| Polystyrene | PS | + | + | ⊕ | ⊕ | ⊕ | + | + | − | ○ | ⊖ | − | + | ⊖ | − | − | ⊖ | + | ⊕ | − | ⊖ | ○ | + |
| Polystyrene, modified | — | + | + | ⊕ | ⊕ | ⊕ | + | ⊕ | − | ○ | ⊖ | − | + | ⊖ | − | − | ⊖ | + | ⊕ | ⊖ | ⊖ | + | + |
| Styrene-butadiene | SB | + | + | ○ | ○ | + | + | | − | − | − | ⊕ | − | − | − | − | | | | − | ⊖ | ○ | + |
| Styrene-acrylonitrile | SAN | + | + | ⊕ | + | + | + | + | − | − | ⊕ | − | ⊕ | − | − | − | ⊖ | + | ⊕ | − | ⊕ | + | + |
| Acrylonitrile-butadiene-styrene | ABS | + | + | ⊕ | + | + | + | + | − | ⊖ | ○ | − | ⊕ | − | − | − | ⊖ | + | + | − | + | + | + |
| Unplasticised polyvinyl chloride | uPVC | + | + | + | + | ⊕ | + | + | ○ | ⊕ | ⊕ | ○ | + | ⊖ | − | − | ⊖ | ⊕ | ⊕ | ⊖ | ⊕ | + | + |
| Polyvinyl chloride + 13% VA | — | | + | ○ | | + | | + | | ○ | | − | + | | − | − | + | + | ⊕ | − | + | | + |
| Polyvinyl chloride + DOP | — | | + | ⊕ | | ⊕ | ○ | + | ○ | ⊕ | | − | ⊖ | ⊖ | | − | + | + | ⊕ | − | − | ○ | ○ |
| Polyvinyl chloride + TCP | — | | + | ⊕ | ⊕ | ⊕ | ○ | + | ○ | ⊕ | | − | ⊖ | ⊖ | | − | + | + | ⊕ | − | − | ○ | ○ |
| Polytetrafluoroethylene | PTFE | + | + | + | + | + | + | + | + | + | + | + | + | + | + | + | + | + | + | + | + | + | + |
| Polytrifluorochloroethylene | PCTFE | + | + | + | + | + | + | + | ⊕ | + | | ⊖ | + | − | ⊖ | + | + | | | ⊕ | ⊕ | + | + |
| Polymethyl methacrylate | PMMA | + | ⊕ | ⊖ | ○ | + | + | + | ○ | ○ | ⊕ | − | ○ | ⊕ | − | ⊖ | + | ○ | ⊖ | ⊖ | ⊕ | + | + |
| Acrylonitrile-methyl methacrylate | AMMA | + | + | + | ○ | ⊕ | ⊕ | | ○ | ○ | ⊖ | + | + | + | − | | | | | ⊕ | + | + | + |
| Chlorinated polyether | — | | + | + | + | + | + | | + | ○ | | + | + | + | + | + | | + | | | + | + | + |
| Polyoxymethylene | POM | + | ⊕ | − | | + | + | + | − | ⊖ | + | ⊖ | + | + | ⊕ | + | ⊕ | | ⊕ | ⊕ | + | + | + |
| Polyphenylene oxide | PPO | + | + | + | | + | + | + | | | | | | | | | | | + | | | | |
| Cellulose acetate | CA | + | + | − | − | ○ | − | + | − | − | + | ⊖ | ○ | + | − | − | ○ | ⊖ | ⊕ | ⊕ | ⊕ | + | + |
| Cellulose acetate with high degree of esterification | CA | + | ⊕ | − | − | ○ | − | + | − | − | + | ⊖ | ○ | + | − | − | + | ⊕ | ⊕ | ⊕ | + | + | + |
| Cellulose acetate butyrate | CAB | + | + | − | − | ⊕ | ○ | + | − | ⊖ | | − | ⊖ | ⊖ | | − | + | ⊕ | ⊕ | − | + | + | + |
| Cellulose propionate | CP | + | ○ | − | − | − | | + | − | | + | − | − | − | − | − | | + | ⊕ | | + | + | + |
| Polycarbonate | PC | + | + | ⊖ | ⊕ | − | − | ⊕ | + | ○ | ⊕ | | ⊕ | − | ⊖ | ⊖ | − | − | ⊖ | | + | ⊕ | + |
| Polyethyleneterephthalate | PETP | | + | ⊕ | | ⊕ | | + | | + | + | ⊖ | ⊕ | + | + | + | | | + | + | + | + | + |
| Polybutyleneterephthalate | PBTP | | ○ | ⊖ | | + | + | + | | | + | ⊖ | + | + | ○ | ⊖ | | | ⊕ | ⊕ | + | + | + |
| Polyamide 6 | PA 6 | + | − | − | − | ⊕ | + | + | − | − | ⊕ | ⊕ | ⊕ | + | + | + | ⊕ | + | ⊕ | ⊕ | + | + | + |
| Polyamide 12 | PA 12 | + | − | − | − | ⊕ | ⊕ | + | − | − | + | ⊕ | ⊕ | + | + | + | ○ | + | ⊕ | ⊕ | + | + | + |
| Polyamide 6.6 | PA 6.6 | + | − | − | − | ⊕ | + | + | − | − | ⊕ | ⊕ | ⊕ | + | + | + | ⊕ | + | ⊕ | ⊕ | + | + | + |
| Polyamide 6.10 | PA 6.10 | + | − | − | − | ⊕ | + | + | | | ⊕ | ⊖ | ⊕ | + | + | + | ⊕ | + | ⊕ | ⊕ | + | + | + |
| Polyamide, aromatic | — | | + | ⊖ | ⊖ | ○ | ⊕ | + | + | | + | + | ⊕ | ⊖ | + | + | ⊕ | ○ | | ⊖ | ⊕ | + | + |
| Polysulphone | — | ⊕ | + | + | | + | + | + | | + | ⊕ | − | + | | | − | | | | − | | | |
| Phenolic resin moulding compounds | PF | + | ○ | − | | ○ | − | | | | ⊕ | ⊕ | ⊕ | ⊕ | ⊕ | | | | ⊕ | ⊕ | + | + | |
| Urea-formaldehyde resin | UF | + | ⊖ | − | | ○ | − | | | | ⊕ | ⊕ | + | ⊕ | ⊕ | | | | ⊕ | ⊕ | + | + | |
| Melamine resin | MF | + | ○ | − | | ⊕ | − | | | | ⊕ | + | ⊕ | ⊕ | ⊕ | | | | ⊕ | ⊕ | + | + | |
| Unsaturated polyester | UP | + | ⊕ | ○ | − | ⊕ | − | + | ⊖ | ⊖ | + | ⊖ | ⊕ | ⊖ | ⊖ | ⊖ | ⊖ | ⊕ | ⊖ | ⊖ | + | + | + |
| Unsaturated polyester, flexible | UP | + | ⊕ | − | − | ⊕ | − | + | ⊖ | ⊖ | + | ⊖ | ⊕ | ⊖ | ⊖ | − | ⊖ | ⊕ | ⊖ | ⊖ | + | + | + |
| Unsaturated polyester, alkali resistant | UP | + | + | ○ | − | ⊕ | +. | + | ⊖ | ⊖ | + | ⊖ | + | ⊖ | ⊖ | ⊖ | ⊕ | ⊖ | ⊖ | + | + | + |
| Epoxy resins | EP | + | ⊕ | | + | ⊕ | ⊕ | + | + | − | | ○ | + | + | ⊖ | ⊕ | ⊖ | ⊕ | + | ⊖ | + | + | + |
| Polyurethane elastomer | PUR | + | ⊕ | ○ | − | ⊕ | ⊕ | + | − | ⊖ | + | ⊖ | ⊕ | ⊕ | ⊕ | + | + | + | ○ | ⊕ | + | + | + |
| Urethane rubber | — | | + | + | ⊖ | + | + | + | + | + | ⊕ | ⊖ | ⊖ | ○ | − | − | | | ⊖ | ⊖ | ○ | ⊕ | ⊕ |

# Index

**All numbers are page numbers**

# Acknowledgements

The authors would like to thank the following for their kindness in supplying samples:

BASF Ludwigshafen:
Herr Bartz
Herr Becker
Herr Brünings
Herr Erhard
Herr Fischer
Herr Kern
Herr Knapp
Herr Koch
Herr Leydecker
Herr Lörtsch
Frau Müller
Herr Pflüger
Herr Retting
Herr Rieger
Herr Romberg
Herr Schmitt
Herr Seiler
Herr Spähn
Herr Strickle
Herr Teege
Herr Theysohn
Herr Weber
Herr Welz
Herr Wurmb

Herr Baumeister,
MD Papierfabriken Dachau
Herr Bednarz,
Siemens AG München
Herr Bejasis,
Siemens AG München
Herr Birnkraut,
Ruhrchemie
Herr Gaube,
Farbwerke Hoechst
Herr Holm,
Bayer Leverkusen
Herr Jantzen,
DFVLR München
Herr Karger,
Sauter Basel
Herr Kern,
Metzeler Kautschuk AG München
Herr Kuhlmann,
DFVLR München
Fräulein Leidenroth,
Daimler Benz AG Stuttgart
Herr Lipowsky,
Krauss Maffei AG München
Herr Nordt,
Wacker Chemie GmbH, Burghausen

Herr Pfaffenhuber,
Wacker-Chemie, GmbH, Burghausen
Herr Razim,
Daimler-Benz AG Stuttgart
Herr Rieger,
Dornier System GmbH, Friedrichshafen
Herr Schneemann,
Chemische Werke Hüls
Herr Schönberger,
MAN München
Herr Sterr,
Varta Batterie AG, Kelkheim
Süddeutsche Kalkstickstoffwerke Trostberg
Herr Ungethüm,
Orthopädische Klinik, München
Herr Wabner,
Technische Universität München
Herr Walter,
Daimler-Benz AG Stuttgart
Herr Weigl,
Institut Papiertechnische Stiftung München
Herr Witte,
Max-Planck-Institut f. Plasmaphysik Garching